Pierce had not been expected to attend the party, so Caprice, normally so self-assured, was taken by surprise when she was literally swept into the arms of this unknown man who made her feel so different, so out of control . . .

Books you will enjoy
by AMANDA CARPENTER

RAGE

Jessica King had loved powerful New York businessman Damien Kent for three years. But now he seemed intent on marrying someone else. How could she bear it?

RECKLESS

Scott Bennett was a threat to Lesley's peace of mind, and she did not want to see him again. But he would not take no for an answer. And then something happened which was more than a threat to her peace of mind—it threatened her life—and his . . .

WAKING UP

For Robbie time seemed to have drifted past, and she still didn't know what she wanted to do with her future. Just because Jason had his future mapped out, didn't mean she should go along with him—but then Jason was acting very strangely these days . . .

CAPRICE

BY

AMANDA CARPENTER

MILLS & BOON LIMITED
15–16 BROOK'S MEWS
LONDON W1A 1DR

*First published in Great Britain 1986
by Mills & Boon Limited*

© Amanda Carpenter 1986

*Australian copyright 1986
Philippine copyright 1986
This edition 1986*

ISBN 0 263 75429 4

*Set in Monophoto Plantin 11 on 12 pt.
01-0886 – 46894*

*Printed and bound in Great Britain by
Collins, Glasgow*

CHAPTER ONE

'I DON'T know,' said Caprice, doubtfully. 'I guess I'd have to think about it.'

'Good God, Cap!' said Roxanne, in an explosion of impatience. Caprice turned her head to look at the brunette who was possibly her closest friend, and the only one who got away with calling her 'Cap'. 'What is there to think about? Either you want to come, or you don't.' Then Roxanne turned suddenly doubtful herself. 'Right?'

Caprice turned back to the outfit she was considering with a vague eye. She had a particular talent for putting all her friends and acquaintances off stride with her preoccupied air, as though she were somewhere else, or at least wishing she was.

And she knew it. That air of distraction was carefully cultivated, and her sudden changes of mood, along with her apparent indecisiveness, kept everyone around her on their toes and hopping. The fact that Roxanne was apparently Caprice's closest friend but that nobody could really tell for sure was just another example of elusiveness that clung to the girl wherever she went. It drove the opposite sex quite crazy, but they seemed to go for it like panting, thirsty dogs, for an entourage of young men from Caprice's acquaintance gathered around her constantly.

She put her slim forefinger to the side of her

mouth, pulling down her lower lip thoughtfully as she stared from Roxanne to the dress she was holding, to the floor and then to the ceiling, and then back to Roxanne. 'We'll just have to wait and see,' she said then, sweetly.

Her friend was flabbergasted, and frankly close to fury. She had jumped to accept the weekend invitation for the two of them, for Jeffrey Langston's family lodge in New England was reputed to be quite luxurious and was most certainly exclusive. Not everyone got an invitation for the weekend, but Caprice didn't seem to realise that.

Roxanne had even let her frustration show, but Caprice had shrugged the irritation aside as if it were no more than a buzzing fly. Sometimes nothing seemed to get to the other girl, and Roxanne wondered briefly if she was as dumb as she sometimes seemed.

But no. One thing that could safely be said about Caprice was that she most definitely was not stupid. She had gained high marks at Vassar yet had hardly ever opened a book, Roxanne remembered, and occasionally would let slip statements that showed a keen working intelligence behind her ever-shifting, changing façade. She had once said of one of the brunette's boyfriends that he had Rox on the brain, and such comments came from her at, to say the least, the most unsettling of times.

Caprice shook the dress by the hanger, making the creases fall out of the static-charged skirt. She was fully aware of what Roxanne was thinking, knew better, most likely, than Roxanne herself, but she let none of it show on her face. Then she held the dress to her front and stared at her reflection in the full length, polished mirror.

A sun-kissed, golden brown face peered back at her, with silver gilt, baby fine hair. It fell to past her shoulders, for the most part fairly straight from the weight of the length, but with wispy tendrils that escaped and framed her face in a luminescent halo. Huge midnight violet eyes were in the middle of this delicately framed, delicately boned face. Perhaps the jaw was rather firm, but nobody ever noticed, for the immense, eloquent eyes were what captured the attention and then gently but quite inexorably held it.

She murmured, imagining herself dancing in the dress under soft lights, 'I think it's the wrong colour for me, don't you?'

With a short, gusty sigh, the brunette turned her attention to the dress also. 'It looks fine to me,' she said.

Those violet eyes turned to her friend, noting the pique. She held the dress next to Roxanne and then dreamily replied, 'Mmm. It would look better on you.'

That attracted the other girl's attention, who then peered into the mirror herself and said, on an interested note, 'Do you really think so?'

'Yes.' Caprice abandoned the dress by shoving it into Roxanne's hands, and then she went along the rest of the small boutique, humming lightly under her breath. On a whim, she threw several different outfits over one arm and headed back to the dressing-rooms to try them all on. Snagged

by the praise Caprice had given her, Roxanne
trailed behind, still clutching the dress.

About forty minutes later, they were both
walking out of the shop, laden down with
packages. Caprice slid a quick glance over to
Roxanne's larger load. If the other girl wondered
why she had been the one to end up with the
larger purchase when it had been Caprice's idea
that they go shopping in the first place, she didn't
say so aloud.

'What now?' asked Caprice lightly, as she
stood in the middle of the pavement and looked
around her. In the sun, her hair nearly
shimmered and sparkled, it blazed so brightly.
'Lunch?'

'I don't know.' Roxanne looked up and down
the street. 'I spent more money than I had
expected to. My allowance for this month is
practically gone, and it's only the nineteenth.'

'No problem.' Caprice's reply was serene, and
she headed down the pavement. 'I'll buy today.'

The restaurant they went to boasted superb
service and exorbitant prices. They were soon
seated, and within no time a bottle of white wine
was ordered and brought to the table, frosty and
dripping from the bucket of ice it resided in. Out
of the corner of her eye, Caprice could see
Roxanne settling back to enjoy the treat, sipping
pleasurably at a glass of the chilled wine, and she
turned her attention to the menu selection,
frowning delicately in indecision. After they had
ordered, Roxanne turned to her and said, 'About
next weekend, Cap——'

'Oh yes, of course,' she said mildly, hiding her

bored resignation. 'I'll go.' She watched as Roxanne stumbled to a halt in the middle of a non-existent argument.

The other girl asked carefully, 'Just like that? You'll go? I thought you wanted to think about it.'

She resisted a caustic retort. 'I have. I think it'll be fun.'

'I—see.'

Caprice smiled very slightly as Roxanne let her mouth hang open as if to say something else, but then apparently changed her mind and shut it tightly. Within a very short time, their lunch was served, cold, delicately flavoured shrimp and leafy salad, and then they turned their conversation to other, mundane things while they ate.

Later, after she had dropped Roxanne at home, she went home herself, humming as Three Dog Night howled over the radio. She pulled, quick and yet neat, into the driveway and to the huge garage, pressing the automatic door opener and watching it swing up with a slight motor whine. She parked her Porsche neatly, and then grabbed for her packages as she climbed out of the car, and entered the huge old colonial house from the garage.

Her parents weren't home yet, so after calling a cheery greeting to their housekeeper, Liz, who was busy in the laundry room, she raced upstairs to her bedroom. Because of the house's age, every bedroom had a fireplace, and exquisite, polished hardwood floors which her mother only occasionally, and not very sincerely, lamented. Caprice had a French tapestry rug spread on the floor of her room which dated back to the late 1800s, with heavy dark wood furniture and a Victorian dresser with a marble top. The colour of the wood reflected a golden warmth whenever she lit a fire in her room.

She carelessly tossed her purchases on to the neatly made, canopied bed and went to her tiny bathroom to work the tangles out of her windblown, silver blonde hair. She stared into the bathroom mirror with a certain amount of wryness.

She was the very first of anyone to admit that she was a rather odd creature. Her mother was Italian, though not full-blooded, having an English grandmother from whom Caprice inherited both hair and eye colouring. But her skin was definitely Latin, as she tanned deeply and quickly to that sun-burnished dark gold without a hint of a freckle anywhere on her slim body. Her first name was an Italian adaptation, and a difficult one to live with at that. But her last name, Hagan, like her father, was decidedly Irish, which was all fair enough considering that they were at least third generation Americans, and part of the huge melting-pot which mixed ethnic groups indiscriminately.

But to saddle her with a name like Caprice was cruelty beyond all cruelties. She tried a frown into the mirror and noticed that it came out petulant, as her frowns always did, so she ironed her brow out again with a sigh. Oh, well, it could have been worse. She could have been named something totally unspeakable, like Olympia, or Myrtle.

The problem was, people tended to form instant impressions about a person from their name, and Caprice certainly didn't lend itself to immediate respect.

To be perfectly frank, she realised, as she walked back to her bedroom and sat on the edge of her bed—and incidentally on the new blouse she'd bought—she really was a bit capricious. She was whimsical, and given to impulse. What was it, really: a case of the name predicting the personality, or the personality fitting itself to the name? She didn't know. Her hand, still clutching the brush, sank slowly to her lap.

For a moment, and only for a moment, something desolate and terribly lonely looked out of the exquisite, immense violet eyes. The whimsical aspect of her personality was only a part of her, she knew. Wasn't it? But then that was all anybody saw in her, even down to her closest friend, so perhaps she was wrong after all. Her expression lightened again, without a single lingering trace of the odd darkness that had showed just a moment before. What difference did it make? Her life was amusing, and diverse.

With a shake of her slim shoulders, she dismissed philosophy from her mind and ran down the stairs in search of her younger brother. Perhaps she could persuade Ricky to play a couple of games of tennis before supper. After that large lunch, she needed to work up an appetite.

She managed to coerce Ricky into playing with her. He had just started college the year before, whereas she had just graduated, but they had one characteristic in common; they were lazing the summer away. They were also well-matched for hard tennis playing, for what Caprice lacked in sheer bulk and power, she made up for in finesse and experience, having played for several years longer than Ricky. But in the end, her large lunch told against her, and she lost rather heavily, much to her brother's mild derision. One commendable characteristic of Ricky's was, however, that he both won and lost with excellent sportsmanship, so they walked back to the kitchen for iced tea in perfect harmony.

Back inside, and blinking against the darkened interior of the kitchen, they at first didn't see Liz, who said, as if appearing from thin air, 'Your mother and father are meeting in the den for drinks at six, and wanted to know if either of you are dining at home.'

'Oh, I'm sorry, Liz!' said Caprice breathlessly, while Ricky, too, apologised. 'I'm eating in tonight, I forgot to tell you.'

'And I'm not,' said her brother, remorsefully. 'Does it mess up your evening meal?'

'Lord, no,' said Liz, well used to such domestic crises.

Caprice and Ricky then headed for the stairs, to clean up. 'Going out with someone?' asked Caprice interestedly, to which her brother grinned.

'Yes, but not in the way you mean. Larry and I are hitting the town tonight.'

'In other words,' she retorted with a laugh, 'you're bar hopping, complete with fake ID, I've no doubt.'

'Hush!' he whispered conspiratorially, looking from left to right with dancing eyes. 'You never know who might be listening.'

She stopped stock still on the second floor landing, and stared at him with fascination. 'No!' she exclaimed. 'Really? You actually have a fake ID? Where'd you get it? Can I see it?'

He took her to his room, and pulled out the identification from his wallet, and she looked it over carefully. It certainly looked quite legitimate, except for the fact that the birth date was set a few years back. To her repeated question, he replied casually, as he stuffed it back into his wallet, 'I got it through one of the fellows at school. Everybody has them. The man who makes them, whoever he is, makes a fortune, no two ways about that.'

She shrugged. 'As long as you're careful.'

Ricky stopped her with a hand on her arm. 'You wouldn't mention this to Mom and Dad, would you?' he asked, searching her eyes.

'Good heavens, no! It's none of my business, unless you drive home roaring drunk some night,' she said airily, dismissing his question with a wave of her hand. 'But you're too level-headed to do that, aren't you?'

'God, yes,' he said with some grimness, as he let go of her. 'I may be wild, extravagant, and utterly devastating to the opposite sex, but I am *not* stupid.'

She glanced at him rather sharply. He was as dark as she was fair, but they shared the same general facial characteristics, and he was indeed quite handsome. She smiled and patted his lean cheek with something of an absent air. 'That you're not, love.'

'No more than you, though you like to act it, sometimes,' he said, unexpectedly shrewd. After searching his eyes, feeling slightly troubled, she merely smiled again and left his bedroom. He shut his door behind her sharply, after slapping her saucily in the rear.

With a glance flashed at her slim gold wristwatch, a graduation present from her parents, she hurried to her own room to shower and change out of her tennis outfit. As it was quite hot, with no breeze at all outside to relieve the mugginess, she slipped on a sleeveless, light blue blouse with a matching pencil-slim skirt and high-heeled sandals. Her breasts were slight and firm, and so she could get away without wearing a bra whenever she felt like it, her usual practice in the summer heat. After brushing her damp hair and letting it hang carelessly loose, she skipped lightly down the stairs and strode for the den in long, easy, athletic paces.

'Hello, Mom, Dad!' she said breezily, stopping for a moment to press a light kiss against her father's greying forehead and to receive one in return. 'Did you both have a good day?'

'Hallo, dear. As good as can be expected,' said Irene, a slight-boned, dark woman with a streak of silver threading her hair at each temple. She was a woman with a placid nature, whose life revolved around the social gatherings and charity functions she was so fond of.

'Huh,' grunted her father. 'Speak for yourself,

Irene. Every damned thing went wrong at the office today. Stupid Witcomb screwed up his account.'

Caprice grinned. Stupid Witcomb was her father's favourite complaint. She sometimes thought that he kept Witcomb around just so that he had something to complain about. The three talked for a little while, sporadically, and her father made her a drink of Bacardi and Coke, with lime. Then Ricky came into the den for a short time, until Larry came to pick him up, and after a flurry of goodbyes and the slam of the front door, things quietened considerably.

When they went in to supper, Caprice said, just remembering, 'Oh, yes. Roxanne and I are going to the Langstons' for the weekend, unless I've managed to forget some vastly important event?'

Her mother thought for a moment. 'No, dear,' she said then. 'Nothing's happening that I know of. Is it to be a party?'

'From what I gather,' she said airily. 'It's to be at their lodge in New England. Roxanne says the place is something else.'

'That's what I've heard, too,' said Irene, with some smugness. 'You should be glad you're going.' She sent a dry look at her father at that, which her mother luckily did not catch. 'But didn't you say something about avoiding Jeffrey for a while?'

She then frowned for a moment, a tiny furrow appearing between her brows which was gone the next second like a cloud passing by on a sunny day. 'Yes, I did,' she admitted, while she worked on her spicy, sauce-covered veal. 'He's entirely too obvious for my taste. But Roxanne is crazy about him. I'm afraid she might get into something she can't handle if she were to go by herself.'

'Something she can't handle?' grunted her father.

She shrugged. 'She's crazy about him, but he isn't crazy about her. If he plays around with her, she might end up getting quite hurt.'

Richard Senior frowned. 'Would young Langston do that?'

She looked to her father and a slow, sweet smile spread across her lips. 'Not if I'm there,' she said.

After a blank moment, he took a bite of veal and then asked, 'Do you mean you plan on keeping an eye on your young girl friend for the whole blasted weekend?'

'Oh no,' she replied, with a little laugh. 'I mean that, if I'm there, Jeffrey won't be paying an inordinate amount of attention to Roxanne.'

'You see,' said Irene, exasperated with her obtuse husband, 'Roxanne is crazy about Jeffrey, but Jeffrey is crazy about Caprice.'

Caprice had forsaken alcohol during the course of supper, and she reached for her iced water, feeling the slick wetness of the sweating glass as she raised the cold drink to her lips. 'Entirely too obvious,' she repeated, not without a sneaking degree of satisfaction.

'And who's chaperoning this weekend fling?' asked her father.

She shook her silver blonde head. 'I haven't

the faintest idea. I would think it's quite respectable, knowing the Langston family. I wouldn't put anything past Jeffrey, but his parents surely wouldn't let him have the full use of the lodge unquestioned. Someone will undoubtedly be there.'

'Langston,' mused Richard, idly. 'What's the older Langston boy doing?'

Caprice didn't know, but Irene did and said, 'I think he's managing the New York branch of the family business now. And he's hardly a boy, dear. Heavens, he must be close to thirty by now.'

'I never met an older brother,' Caprice said then. 'What's his name?'

'Pierce, I believe,' replied her mother, absently. 'And it's really not surprising you haven't met him, dear. Not really your age group, is he?'

The next day, Caprice received a phone call from Roxanne, who wanted to make plans for the weekend. She listened as the other girl chattered about flights from Byrd Field, but then interrupted gently.

'Rox, I don't want to fly.' She made her voice sound slightly plaintive.

A pause. 'What, did you want to drive up? Really, Cap, it would be much easier to just get that flight out of Richmond, and much quicker, too.'

'Yes, you're right of course,' she replied immediately.

The satisfaction was evident in the other girl's voice. 'So shall I book two flights on Friday for us?'

Flying would be much easier, but it would also

leave them trapped for the entire weekend
without independent transportation, and she said
slowly, 'No, I don't think so. Thanks anyway.'

Swift alarm now, in Roxanne's voice. 'What do
you mean? You haven't changed your mind about
going, have you?'

Caprice smiled at the hall stairs, where she
happened to be staring. 'You go ahead and book a
flight for yourself,' she replied, understandingly.
'I believe I'm going to drive.'

Friday dawned bright and clear. She had her
suitcase already packed, so, after dressing in
khaki shorts and a rich cream sleeveless shirt, it
was a simple matter of running downstairs to sit
down at the light breakfast Liz prepared for her,
and then throwing her suitcase in the back of the
Porsche. The day was already quite hot, so she
took out the sun roof before leaving the driveway,
and about fifteeen minutes later she was pulling
up at her friend's house and leaning on her horn.
For a few moments the front door didn't budge
an inch, and then it exploded open with the force
of Roxanne's exuberant exit. The brunette
skipped down the steps lightly, suitcase in hand,
and was in obviously better spirits than she had
been when Caprice had last talked with her.

'I decided to forgive you,' said Roxanne with a
puff, as she tossed her suitcase along with
Caprice's.

'That's very generous of you. Get in. Forgive
me for what, though? I think I've forgotten.'

'For driving, idiot. You knew I wouldn't fly
without you.' Roxanne climbed in and ran a
covetous hand over the passenger seat. The

brunette had been frankly envious of Caprice's car ever since her father had given it to her for her twenty-first birthday.

'Yes, well, it's a lovely day, and we're going to have a marvellous time,' said Caprice a bit absently, as she backed out of the driveway. 'I hope you didn't forget the map?'

'Of course not.' Roxanne patted her handbag complacently. 'It's right here, never fear.'

'That's good,' Caprice replied cheerfully, as she pressed down the accelerator and the car gained speed. Hot wind whipped through her hair. 'I hope you can read it. I never could make sense out of a map.'

Later that day, Caprice looked out of her bedroom window at the lush wooded greenery that surrounded the Langstons' large house. Lodge was scarcely the word for it; it was nearly as big as her own family's house, and this was used only for holidays. She shook her head. Her family was what one might call rich, but this was a totally different meaning to the word.

She and Roxanne did have a lovely drive north, arriving with sunny spirits, a bit of glow on their noses and arms from the open sun roof, and windblown hair. They found Jeffrey's parents in residence, along with several of the weekend guests who had already arrived, so the house was lively, with the promise of a party and dancing later in the evening. She took one more look around the room she'd been given, a lovely one, though quite small. That didn't matter to her in the slightest, for she was simply thankful she didn't have to team up with one of the other girls.

Roxanne was located across the hall from her, so, after she had brushed her silver gilt hair into some semblance of order, she strolled across and rapped on the door.

Rox's voice called out for whoever it was to enter, and Caprice stuck her head around the edge of the door. 'I'm ready to go back down,' she said. 'Are you?'

The brunette was touching up her make-up, and peering at herself closely. 'How do I look?' she asked through stiff lips, as she ran her lipstick over them. 'No, don't answer that. I don't think I want to know. Yes, I'm ready if you are.'

Caprice's laughter pealed merrily down the halls. 'Quit acting like a martyr!' she exclaimed. 'Come on. We're here to enjoy ourselves, right?'

And she led the way down the stairs, lightly skipping. When they reached the large living room, they ran smack into Jeffrey, a handsome, dark fellow, who laughingly caught at Caprice's arms to keep her from being bowled over. 'There you two are!' he said, still laughing. 'I was just coming to get you.'

Some of the people she knew, and some she didn't. As she set about getting to know each of them without delay, there was soon a slight but definite gravitational shift in the room. One by one the young men wandered over, lured by Caprice's flashing, laughing eyes and light voice. With four men and four women, ages from early twenties to about twenty-five or six, there was obviously supposed to be some pairing, but that seemed to be upset at once.

Perhaps the reason why the other three women didn't get extremely annoyed with Caprice was because she never did quite give any one man too much attention. She flitted from person to person, watchful of the atmosphere under her careless façade, and talked with as much enthusiasm to each of the young women as she did with the men, so that soon everyone was jabbering quite comfortably with everyone else, and nobody was exactly sure how it came about.

Besides Jeffrey, there was another dark, slim man named Lane Randall. Then she knew the blond, rather stocky, good-natured man named Emory, and a redhead named Ralph. Of the women, Caprice was the only blonde, the others being varying shades of brunette, and one woman, Petra, being particularly ravishing. Both Caprice and Roxanne knew the other, Gwynne, and for that reason Caprice tried to go out of her way to be especially nice to Petra.

Dinner came and went, an informal affair consisting of cold meats and salads, and the talk was very general. Jeffrey's parents were lovely people who made themselves as unobtrusive as possible, with the kind of tact that Caprice silently appreciated. Afterwards, everyone made a general exodus to their rooms to change for the party which started at eight. Several local people had been invited, and it was to be quite large.

The house was located at the shoreline of a deep, large, sky blue lake, and Caprice hoped that the party would spill outdoors so that they could

take advantage of the cooling night breeze. She
held two dresses in her hands, one a simple light
lavender affair, and the other also made of a light
summer material but not at all simple, being a
frothy white confection and nearly (as Ricky had
said) good enough to eat. She dithered over
which to wear, and then laughed at herself, for
she would have to wear the other the next night
anyway, and so she laid down the white
confection and put away the lavender.

Fifteen minutes later, she whirled in a circle
and the skirt flared from her wasp-slim waist,
three layers of transparent tulle falling to settle
against her knees. She patted her hair, which was
arranged in her best French braid, and then with
a small, satisfied smile she descended the stairs
just in time to meet the first wave of guests.

The evening went splendidly. Jeffrey did not
pay too much attention to Caprice, so Roxanne
didn't feel slighted. The back garden was, much
to Caprice's delight, lit with low-hanging,
yellowish lanterns which were reflected off the
blackened waters of the lake until it looked like
the whole scene held a countless array of lights.
The breeze blew cool and refreshing, and the
talking, laughing guests spilled from large, open
glass doors which led to a roofless veranda. After
some time, music was played over stereo speakers
positioned so that the songs filled the open area.

Caprice took a position next to the soft lapping
water, leaning against the sturdy, waist-high
wooden rail as she watched the dancing. Just to
her left was a pier of the same sturdy wood as the
rail, red stained, and several small boats were

moored to it, quietly bumping against each other. Soon she was joined by others, and the small group held a confusion of witty, enjoyable talk.

She had danced with every male weekend guest, and Jeffrey also, and then she had danced with almost every other man besides, laughingly, stepping as light as the breeze that touched at her warm cheeks. To one side was a table holding beer for those who cared for it, wine, which was more to her own taste, and an array of soft and mixed drinks. For some reason the dancing had trickled down to just a few. She leaned back against the rail, sipped at her glass of wine, and listened to the talk around her.

She could never say why the impulse grabbed her, later. But it came as they always came, on a fit of quick-welling, inexplicable boredom, incomprehensible to her and so never talked about. She knew the impulses were why other people thought she was whimsical and flighty, but she couldn't seem to curb them.

She set her glass down with a sharp click on to the flat wide top of the wooden rail, and pushed herself away from it. Then she drew herself to attention, and politely, ludicrously, addressed the empty air in front of her. 'Dear sir, would you care to dance with me?'

A neat sidestep and she was the gentleman, responding as courteously to the inviting lady, 'Why yes, madam, I would be delighted.'

She moved back to the role of the lady. 'Thank you, sir. I am much obliged.' Her arms curved up gracefully, holding her invisible partner. He would be blond, she thought, fleetingly fanciful.

Tall, blond and utterly gorgeous. Polite.
Passionate. Perfect.

At first there had been a blank silence from
everyone, and then a few of the men made as if
they would laughingly partner her, but she was
already stepping into an old-fashioned ballroom
waltz, swinging wide, sweeping graceful and
swirling, making her white dress billow from her
waist in the night wind. The breeze feathered at
the light, silvery, loose hair at her temples, and
the lighting from the open glass doors spilled
over her, at one moment making her a slim
silhouette, at another, highlighting her perfectly.
Her slim neck rose from her white shoulders with
the slight curve of a swan's, and she was
distinctly seen to be talking away to her invisible
partner. Everyone from the group watched her,
entranced and highly entertained. Everyone saw
the imminent collision, except for Caprice.

She whirled around, and bumped right into
someone. With a laughing gasp, her arms
collapsed and clutched at the real flesh and blood
someone she had run into, and hard arms went
around her waist in response. She tumbled out an
apology.

And looked up. The man who lightly held her
was half obscured from the light spilling out of
the house, and half lit. She caught a glittering
impression of dark bright eyes under a black fall
of straight, glossy hair. His face—what she could
see of it—was vaguely familiar, and arresting. He
was taller than she, and slim also, and not looking
at all surprised to be holding a piece of white fluff
and froth.

A slow smile creased whitely over his lips, lighting his whole countenance. Something kicked in her chest like a captured bird. 'Oh, well,' he said, and his voice was low and well modulated. 'If you really need a partner . . .'

She began to smile in response, as she tilted her head a little to one side, like a diffident bird. 'Sir,' she said sedately, immensely thankful he couldn't determine her inner reaction, 'I would be charmed.'

They began the waltz steps, as one.

CHAPTER TWO

As they circled in that grand style, she leaned comfortably back against the steady, hard arm at her waist and smiled at her unknown partner, her sudden, inexplicable boredom for the moment quite erased. His dark head was bent, angled to her, as he watched her face in the quick golden flashes that spilled over them from the lanterns hung in the trees.

'Tell me,' he said, and she raised her brows. He started to smile again, eyes sparkling. 'Do you ride away on a pumpkin at midnight?'

'Goodness, no,' she replied lightly, feeling dizzy. 'I brought a car. Besides, I'm not leaving at midnight. I'm staying the weekend.' She tried to focus more sharply on his flickering features, finding she liked the feel of his firm hold on her, and the smooth grace with which he danced. 'And you? Are you one of the neighbourhood guests? I don't believe we've been introduced.'

'No, we haven't,' he said as lightly, watching her. 'I'd have remembered if we had.' That brought a secret smile to her lips. He knew his party patter. 'I'm Jeffrey's brother, Pierce, come from New York for a bit of relaxation. No one told me there was to be a weekend party.'

'Don't feel bad,' she said, confidingly, and she leaned close to him. For a brief instant she inhaled a fresh, attractive scent that was his aftershave. 'I was told just a few days ago, myself.'

He looked indulgent, amused. They circled, now somewhat far from the house and lakeside, and he came to stop underneath one of the glowing lanterns, letting his hands rest at her waist as she twinkled up at him with her enormous, midnight violet eyes. She could feel the weight and the warmth of those large hands through her thin dress. 'Well, I've told you mine,' he said, running his eyes over her face, lingeringly. 'Do you, by any chance, have a name of your own?'

She laughed, finding suddenly that the party was quite enjoyable, and that the weekend might indeed end up being, to say the least, interesting. Letting one light finger trail down the side of her impromptu partner's lean cheek, savouring the feel of warm skin, she then pulled gently out of his arms and turned away. She called over her shoulder, voice threaded with teasing, 'Yes, I do.'

As she walked across the lawn, she could feel his gaze on her back. Their little confrontation had been watched by many interested eyes, among whom was Jeffrey, who didn't appear too pleased at his older brother's unexpected arrival. Caprice went over to her wine glass, still precariously perched on the wooden rail, and she sipped at the drink sedately while Roxanne neatly swooped from around one of the young men, to reach her side.

'So, how was it?' she asked, her eyes avid.

Caprice glanced at the brunette and then away, and as she hadn't liked the question or how

Roxanne had posed it, she let her eyes go vague.
'The wine?' she murmured, looking at her glass
in some surprise. 'Why, it's delicious, of course.
Haven't you tried it yet?'

'No, stupid! I meant the dance with Pierce
Langston.' With difficulty, Roxanne tried to keep
her voice down.

'Quite an accident,' replied Caprice, flippantly.

'Honey, that was no accident,' responded
Roxanne, rather drily. For the moment, the two
girls were as if they were alone, as nobody
seemed to be paying any attention to them. 'He
deliberately stepped into your path.'

Another leap in her chest, as when she had
bumped into Pierce, only this one was much
stronger. As her violet eyes swivelled sharply to
her friend, she thought the sensation wasn't at all
pleasant. 'Are—you sure?'

'Everybody noticed,' whispered Roxanne, while
she appeared to be staring interestedly into the
dark lapping waters. 'Jeffrey was so jealous, he
nearly turned bright green right in front of our
eyes.'

That brought even more disconcertment to
her, and she stared at Roxanne for some moments
before saying softly, 'You know that he's—
he's——'

'Infatuated with you, yes. He's certainly
made no secret of it,' said the brunette, suddenly
acid. 'That was why he invited us, didn't you
realise?'

She blinked. She wanted to say that she'd
hoped Roxanne hadn't, but as there was no point
in being so bluntly honest, especially with the

possibility that they might be overheard, she merely shrugged it off. Her patent unconcern for Jeffrey's affections made the brunette relax after a moment, and even regret her acidic tone. Just because Jeffrey was infatuated with Caprice, didn't mean that Caprice returned the compliment. Half the men at the party tonight were infatuated with the blonde, and the other half were clearly indulgent. Roxanne's irritation melted away.

Caprice glanced at her friend, saw the return of good humour in the other girl's expression, and was pleased. She hated it when other people were angry at her, especially when the cause for their anger wasn't her fault. She tossed off the last bit of wine in her glass, hiccuped before she could help it, and they both laughed.

There was a sound of slow footsteps. Jeffrey's pleasant, teasing voice said next to Caprice, 'And what's the joke you two are sharing so secretively?'

She looked at him. His large dark eyes were full of admiration and dazzlement as he stared at her. After a quickly flicked glance, he hadn't so much as smiled at Roxanne, who was near to drooling over his handsome, smooth features. A quiver of anger shook through her at his utter obtuseness, and her friend's total lack of taste. She flipped out a hand and twitched at his dark tie. 'You, darling,' she said, sweetly malicious, and she strolled away.

Jeffrey stared after her, astonished and half angry at her rather too sharp reply. Then, in a fit of pique, he turned to lavish his attention on an all too willing Roxanne, who didn't know or care why her friend had taken it into her head to make one of those all too uncomfortable retorts of hers.

Caprice turned to observe her handiwork from an outside table, where she busied herself refilling her wine glass. The two she had just left were close together, dark head to dark head while they animatedly talked about something. Good, she thought, turning away with an unconscious toss of her head. Maybe he would pester Rox all weekend, and quit bothering her. Rox would more than welcome it. His older brother was nowhere to be seen, she found, as she looked around casually. She moved her nearly bare shoulders. Oh well, the party was becoming dull anyway. Perhaps she would go upstairs early.

Then Emory joined her, his fair complexion rather flushed in the yellow spilling light from their direct right. She let her gaze run swiftly over him while she smiled an ingenuous welcome. He was immaculately groomed, and she could faintly smell his expensive cologne from where she stood. He was even handsome, in a fleshy sort of way. She couldn't think why he reminded her of nothing so much as an overgrown puppy.

She chattered with him for a while, but, when Petra drifted over, she was soon able to extricate herself from the pair with a rambling comment about the boats tied to the pier, as she walked that way. She stepped carefully on the planks, as a vivid image of herself tripping by catching one of her stiletto heels in the inch-wide gaps came to mind, and then stood at the end of the pier

looking over the lake. The breeze felt slightly
damp on her cheeks, and refreshingly cool, while
the water looked black and impenetrable, with
rippling gold reflections of light dancing across
its surface.

She stared down at the water dreamily. If her
eyes went murky, or a frown began to etch itself
between her sleek winged brows, she would have
claimed laughingly to be unaware of the fact.
There was nothing to brood about anyway, in
weedy lake water. Just because the surface looked
impenetrable like black onyx, while to go
underneath would be to find a whole different,
complex world——

The boards creaked. She turned her head
slightly, and listened to the sounds of someone
approaching. Too heavy to be a woman. She
composedly lifted her glass and sipped from it,
her eyes blinking now, almost sleepily. The man
stopped just beside her, and awareness of his
presence tingled in her mind. She suddenly
knew, without looking, who it was.

'Thrown together by capricious fate,' said
Pierce, drolly, and she flicked one startled,
wincing glance at him. He was smiling crookedly,
and at her pained expression he quietly laughed.
'Sorry. I couldn't resist. You probably hear
things like that all the time.'

She felt her pulse quicken, pleasantly. He had
obviously asked someone about her name.
'Rather a lot,' she admitted, and cradled her glass
in one slender hand. She sent another glance to
him, finding it difficult to see his face clearly.
They were both facing away from the hanging

lights, which put their fronts into shadow. His
back was well lit, showing the sleek and elegant
lines of his dark tailored suit, and the shape and
tilt of the back of his dark head. He turned his
gaze to her then, and his cheekbone, corner
eyelashes, and jaw were lit briefly, slanting
golden colour. He was still faintly smiling.

'Why the name Caprice?' he asked, tucking his
hands into his pockets, the suit jacket turned
back. His white shirt was shadowy. She belatedly
realised why he looked so familiar; in a very
superficial way, he looked like Jeffrey, yet with
hardened maturity and the beginning of lines.

She let herself laugh, not too loudly, not too
long, and it sent a light tinkling shiver over the
silent lapping water. 'My mother had four false
alarms when she was pregnant and overdue with
me. Every time they rushed her to the hospital,
all tense and worried over it, because I was her
first, they didn't know quite what to expect, all
those sorts of things. When she finally went into
real labour, they calmly took their time getting
ready and leaving—too much suspense, I guess,
during the first four times, and they had quite
exhausted all their anxiety. I was born five blocks
from the hospital. My father likes to say that I've
been as difficult to predict ever since.'

'A difficult legacy to live with, I should think,'
he murmured, low as the lapping of the dark
waters.

It brought her head around with an almost
painful snap of the neck. He was brooding, eyes
on the end of the pier, which was right at his feet.
She let her eyes travel down the length of his

lean, elegant body, to his sleek, black shoes. They were planted somewhat apart from each other, unconsciously proud. A shiver ran delicately down her exposed nape to her spine. She couldn't think when she had ever heard anyone react in such a way to the explanation of why her parents had named her Caprice. Everyone always laughed.

She heard herself say gently, 'I seem to have a talent for it.'

His downbent head turned sideways as he shot a glance at her. After a moment, he stirred and asked, 'And what are you thinking as you stand here and stare into murky lakewater? I can assure you, at night it is very cold.'

She replied lightly, as she lifted a slim hand to ineffectually tuck back some of the wisps that had escaped from her French braid, 'I was wondering what's at the other end, of course. Doesn't everyone?'

He replied, with some dryness, 'As I haven't met half the people who have been here at one time or other, I have no idea. I usually steer clear of the lodge on weekends.' A slight pause, as she digested that. She wondered, then, why he had come up from New York on this particular weekend. Perhaps he had really done it on a whim, that capriciousness of fate he'd joked about. She was pulled out of her idle reverie as he turned to her, businesslike, and suggested, 'So why don't we find out what's at the other end?'

She looked and felt startled as she blinked back at him. 'Do you mean—right now?' She sent her gaze back over the waters, and then said, somewhat doubtfully, 'Would we be able to see it, in night time?'

'Who knows?' he replied, with a grin. 'Care to give it a try?'

She regarded him smilingly, fully aware of the light which left part of her face for his interested inspection. The visible violet eye sparkled with amusement. 'I forgot,' she accused. 'You already know what's on the other side.'

His quiet laughter sounded then. 'Yes, but you don't.'

'Well, then, what are we waiting for?'

But they had to choose a boat. He turned and frowned thoughtfully at the collection tied at the pier. When he seemed to hesitate close by a motor boat, she pleaded, 'Oh, please. No motors. It would ruin everything.'

He raised his black eyebrows. 'Lady, that is a big lake.'

'Well,' she said, wavering. Then she continued bravely, 'I'll row.'

This time his laughter wasn't quiet at all, but a shout which carried over the water. He then walked over to stand by one boat, as she carefully came his way. 'Well, then, this will have to be it.'

'I should get rid of my glass,' she said, eyeing it.

'Oh, no, you don't,' he told her, with grim amusement. 'If you walk over that lawn, you may never come back again alone. I've seen how Jeffrey and his friends act around you. Come here, you can bring it with you.'

She took the last two steps to reach his side, and as he contemplated the rowing boat, and then her fragile, high-heeled sandals, he turned to take her firmly under the elbows. 'Stiffen your arms,' he warned, and she did so. Then he swung her into the boat, only letting go as he made sure she had her balance and a bracing hold of the side. Then he divested himself of his suit jacket, leaving it folded haphazardly on the pier, and stepped lightly into the boat also. He had to pass by her to reach the rowing seat, his thigh brushing her bare shoulder, and then he said, 'OK, here we go. Can you reach back and loosen that knot?'

She did, and found she could reach it quite comfortably. 'There we go,' she said, her voice sounding underneath the pier and echoing oddly. 'We're free.'

'Wait. Why don't you grab my jacket?' suggested Pierce then, a quiet-voiced unknown. 'You might want it after a bit, on those sleeveless arms.'

'Thanks, I will.' That wasn't the pier, she thought, with another shiver. That strange breathless note was all her own. She took his jacket and draped it over her shoulders, finding the shoulder width far too big and quite lovely for snuggling deep into. She could smell the same, faint, fresh scent as before, and she stealthily inhaled deeply.

He loosened the oars and, with a shoulder-flexing shove off one of the other moored boats, they shot out so that he could begin rowing. She leaned back on one hand while she sipped from her wine and looked around her lazily. Very probably the hard seat was dirty, and her dress

would be rendered unwearable until she had a
chance to wash it, but she didn't care.

The only sounds were the dipping of the oars,
continual and rhythmic, and the wafting music
from the party which carried for a startling
distance. The air smelled fresh, slightly wet, and
she was thankful for his jacket as a cooler wind
chilled her. She said then, 'Are you warm
enough? Here you are, doing all the work, and
I'm snuggled deep into your suit coat.'

'Don't trouble yourself, I'm quite warm,' he
reassured rather quickly, as she made as if to
take off the jacket. She subsided then, and after
a bit he spoke again, very quietly. 'Are you
awake?'

'Mmm,' she said, and then laughed. 'Yes, but a
bit muddled from the wine, I think. I had some
at supper, and it's starting to go to my head.
Sorry.'

She could hear the smile in his voice. 'Don't
be. As long as you're not roaring drunk. See
those lights, along the edge to your right? Those
are other houses. Our neighbours don't take too
kindly to a lot of ruckus on the water late at
night. The sound carries over to them.'

'Well, please don't worry about me, then,'
she said, with a light, hand-covered yawn. 'I
don't get drunk. I fall asleep. It can be utterly
mortifying.' While he chuckled, she paused to
look at the oars with some distaste. They were
already far out from the Langstons' property and
coming to the other end of the lake, which was
peaceful and dark, though by no means quiet.
A multitude of crickets positively screeched

from the undergrowth. 'I suppose I should offer to row back.'

Another low chuckle. He neatly swung the boat around and began to slowly row them back. 'I won't hold you to that promise. You do realise that you'll probably be a bit dingy on your backside?'

'Heavens, yes, but who cares?' she said, impatient and light. 'I'll just sneak upstairs by the back way. Does the house have a back way?'

'We'll figure out something for you,' he said amusedly. 'If you like, we can edge past everyone, back to back.'

She grinned. They had passed around the slight bend in the lake, and the low-hung golden lanterns were visible, far over the dark waters like a magical domain. Faint music and laughter wafted to them on the breeze, and Pierce sat facing her, a blackened, impenetrable figure as he tirelessly rowed them back.

She hardly recognised the impulse, or the wistfulness that was too audible in her voice as she said, 'I suppose we have to go back?'

The faint light illuminated her features, flickering light and dusky shadow. Her silver hair in wisps around her face blurred her features like an old photograph, and her eyes glistened at once brilliant and dark. She thought she saw his black head move sharply, and there was a moment as he apparently stared at her, his flexing shoulders still.

He said, rather oddly, 'I don't think there's anywhere we could pull to shore. It's too muddy, with tangled weeds. You'd never make it in those shoes, otherwise I do believe I'd be tempted.'

She was appalled at the seriousness with which he had taken that wistful note, and the seriousness with which she had meant it. She shook loose of the strange feeling that had gripped her, and laughed carelessly as though she'd meant it as a joke the whole time. 'Well, then, if we must go back, we must. Besides, I've finished my wine.'

A pause. Then he picked up rowing again. 'Then by all means,' he responded, lightly teasing. 'That clinches it. But which is it, to return the glass or refill it?'

'I haven't decided yet,' she replied composedly.

They glided to the pier smoothly, and Pierce expertly steered the boat between the two where it had been tied before, giving one last gentle backward pull on the oars to send the flattened end towards the rope. She reached it easily, looked up to the pier, and then down, doubtfully, to her high-heeled sandals. She said hesitantly, 'Ah, I don't think I'll be able to climb out in these shoes.'

'Hold on,' he said, his voice quiet under the noise of the nearby party. He stood, balancing easily, and then told her, 'Slide over to the side. There you go. Now, I'll step out, and then help you, all right?'

'All right.' He lightly passed her, a lean black-clad figure, his hand going to her shoulder to steady himself. She held quite still. Then he heaved himself up, and squatted to fasten the rope more securely. He turned, still bent.

'All set, pretty fairy?' he asked, extending a

hand to her. She removed his jacket, and handed
that to him first.

'I'd never forgive myself if that ended in the
water,' she told him wryly, as he took it and laid
it aside. His hand was offered again, and she had
to laugh as she laid the wine glass in his palm.
She watched as he set it on the protective cloth of
his jacket, and then gave him both her free hands
when he turned to her for the third and final
time. She saw him smile. With his help, she stood
in the boat and attempted the large step to the
pier. Her heel slipped on the smooth wood,
catching in the crack, and one of his arms snaked
around her waist to lift her bodily the rest of the
way.

Heartbeat, one, two, strong and steady, beating
against her breast, against his shirt. The two of
them, utterly still for a moment, his arm still
hard, tight about her, her hands to his shoulders
for balance, his head bent to her while her face
was upturned, looking at him searchingly.
Looking for what? She didn't know, but she had
a sudden, powerful impression that it was very
important, if she could only understand. Vital,
one might say, like his body warmth under the
white shirt, his light breathing, that lean body
flush with hers. She felt flustered, suddenly too
warm, an uncomfortable, uncharacteristic reaction, and she gently pulled away from him,
looking anywhere but his face. His hand lingered
for a moment at the back of her waist, and then
fell away.

She turned, as if at random, and stared back
over the dark lake. 'I enjoyed it,' she said

quickly, her hands clasped in front of her. Then she turned to stare to shore, and she made a sudden bid for escape from this quiet, unknown man, and her unknown, stirred emotions. 'Thank you.'

He followed just behind. 'You're quite welcome. My pleasure.'

And then she knew a strange and futile anger, one that brightened her eyes into amethyst stones and brought a light flush to her cheekbones, for she saw their little excursion for what it really was. There had been nothing but two people enjoying a brief respite from the social chatter of a light-hearted party, strangers to each other and rather indifferent. Nothing but that, and her own foolishness. Her eyes went over him as they came to brighter light. A youngish man still, perhaps thirty years of age, already distinguished looking, with quick observant eyes and an apparent intelligence. There was comprehension and responsibility in this man. What in the world would he and she ever see in each other?

Emory and Ralph, talking together languidly, saw both of them, and they immediately approached. 'Where have you been?' asked Emory with a smile. 'I noticed you were gone several minutes ago, and nobody knew where you'd vanished to.'

'We explored the lake!' exclaimed she, with an extravagant gesture, her eyes sweeping Pierce's but not quite meeting his. She laughed and then took hold of her skirt, trying to twist it so that she could see the back. Then she mourned, 'And I got my skirt dirty.'

'Quite the adventurer,' said Ralph mockingly, and the two chuckled to see her turn in a circle. She put her outspread hands behind her in a concealing fashion, and wore a half guilty, half sheepish expression.

'I'd better go upstairs and see if I can clean this,' she said then. She turned to a silent, rather reserved Pierce, and told him, 'Thank you again. Oh, good! You've got the glass. I'd forgotten it. Well, I'll say good night then. See you all in the morning. If you happen to see Rox, would you tell her I've gone up?' Then with a smile given to them all impartially and a flurry of good nights from the men in response, she abandoned her abashed pose and lightly strode inside to skip up the stairs and to her room.

The three stared after her. Still laughing, Ralph shook his head and said, 'Rowing around in a dirty boat, in a dress that must have cost a fortune!'

'That's Caprice,' said Emory, rocking back and forth on his heels. Then both the younger men looked at Pierce, who was expensively clad in his dark sober business trousers, his jacket hooked carelessly on one finger and draped over one white shoulder. Pierce just twirled an empty, long-stemmed glass between two fingers and smiled, imperturbably.

In her room, Caprice stripped and then slipped into a rose silk pyjama suit. She inspected the back of her white skirt, her lower lip pinched between her teeth in thought. An obvious streak of greyish brown marred the top layer, and she then consulted the cleaning directions on the inside tag. Wouldn't it be just her luck that the dress was to be dry cleaned? It was indeed, and she had to content herself with shaking the dress as vigorously as she could before hanging it in the wardrobe. The material was too delicate. She didn't dare risk wetting it down.

She then turned her attention to her hair, and took out the pins that held the braid in place. She loosened it, and then took a brush to her hair hard, wondering why she felt as though everything that had happened that evening had gone flat. Sighing, she ran her fingers through the ripples from the confining braid, and rubbed at the back of her head.

There was a knock at the door. Curiously, she went to answer it, thinking perhaps that Roxanne might want to talk about the party, but as the door swung open, she found an older woman on the other side, with a smile on her thin face. Caprice smiled back. 'Yes?'

'Miss Hagan? I'm Mrs Vandusen, the Langstons' housekeeper.'

Now she remembered the other woman, and she threw the door open wide as she held out her hand. 'Yes, of course. What can I do for you?' she asked as they shook hands, liking the housekeeper's strong grip. She wondered what on earth the other woman could possibly want.

'It's actually what I might be able to do for you,' said Mrs Vandusen, her eyes warming from Caprice's friendliness. 'Pierce mentioned to me that you needed someone to see to your dress?'

'Oh!' For a moment, she felt quite flustered. Recovering, she grimaced wryly. 'Oh, yes, well, it was my own fault, I'm afraid. I've looked at it, and it must be dry cleaned, so I'll have to see to it when I get home.'

'No problem,' said the housekeeper cheerfully. 'I can get it taken care of tomorrow, if you'd like.'

'But—You've so much work to take care of, with guests staying the weekend,' protested Caprice.

That made the older woman smile. 'Bless you, but honestly, I do this all the time. It's really no bother.'

'Well,' she said, wavering. She went to the wardrobe and drew out the dress. She said, as Mrs Vandusen inspected the skirt, 'It's not as if it's stained, or anything. It's just that the skirt is so white, the slightest dirt shows.'

'That's not bad at all,' said the housekeeper. 'I'll have this done in no time.' She took the hanger.

Caprice followed her to the door, saying gratefully, 'Thank you very much.'

Mrs Vandusen turned around as she stepped out into the hall. 'You're very welcome,' she said, warmly.

Someone was approaching from the staircase. The upstairs floor plan was a basic 'L' shape, and Caprice's room was on the outside corner so that she could look down each hall without difficulty from her door. She glanced towards the stairs as the housekeeper turned away with her white dress, and Pierce appeared, strolling apparently for whichever room was his, shirt casually unbuttoned at his throat.

Suddenly, though she was more decently clad

than she'd been in her dress, Caprice felt
self-conscious and longed to step quickly back into
her room. But he had already seen them both and
was coming their way, a slight, enigmatic smile
touching at those male lips. He ran his eyes over
her, and a light of appreciation touched at his eyes.

For Caprice, it was the first time she'd seen
him in full light, and something hit her midriff
with a nearly audible thump. The way he held his
dark head spoke of someone well used to
authority, and the controlled set of his expression,
the self-possession in his stance, revealed his
maturity. The glimpses of that lean elegance
she'd got outside hit her full on. A poised man,
this.

'I hope everything's been taken care of?' he
asked, turning his smile to Mrs Vandusen, who
beamed back.

'Yes, sir. Good night, to the both of you,' said
the housekeeper, and she continued down the
hall.

She said, subdued, 'Thank you for sending her
up.'

He turned back to her fully, and said quietly, 'I
hope she can get it clean. It's a lovely dress.'

Her heart hammered, her chest was restricted,
her mouth was dry. Damnation, what was wrong
with her? She wasn't in control, that was what
was wrong with her. 'Well,' she said, trying to
breathe deep. 'I guess I'll say good night again.'

'Of course,' he said, as if continuing, and he
tilted his head to the side, letting his eyes linger
on her figure. He paused, deliberately, and then
smiled slowly, devastatingly, and his eyes

returned to her waiting, wary face. Those eyes, those dark eyes. 'There is something to be said for rose.'

Her cheeks flamed hot, and her eyes flashed brief and brilliant before she ducked her head and muttered something quick and incoherent. Then she rushed back inside her room and slammed the door shut behind her. Appalled by her lack of restraint, her lack of composure over a simple comment, she pressed her fingers to her face in mortification.

She didn't hear footsteps outside, but that was probably a combination of carpeting and her door's thickness. At least she was in privacy now, to think over the evening and find it surprisingly hard to get a certain man, a perfect stranger, out of her mind.

Her heart started a slow, hard pounding then, as she turned her head slightly to catch the sound of quiet footsteps walking away from outside her door, several moments later.

CHAPTER THREE

A SPARKLING clear morning, with sights and smells and sounds wafting through her open bedroom window, making her breathe deep in appreciation. An early morning, the sunshine lighting the dark green grass to silver white and dispersing the pre-dawn chill, making her long to be outside in the warmth. A quiet morning, since most, if not all, were still abed after the party the evening before, and as Caprice dressed in tan slacks with a lemon yellow rugby shirt, she could not resist sneaking down the stairs and outdoors.

The air was more chilly than she had expected, and she rubbed her arms under the short sleeves with a shiver. To her left, the wind took hold of a few pine trees and shook them, sending a light scatter of browning needles to carpet the ground underneath. She walked around the lodge aimlessly, feeling curiously lonely at that quiet time in that strange place.

She had slept uneasily, with a restlessness and dissatisfaction that was unusual for her. Before she had slipped into that troubled rest, she had asked herself a myriad of questions with an unaccustomed, sharp bitterness. What was she doing here? What was she doing with her life? Why should she feel a lack of substance and depth to her existence now, of all times?

In the early morning sunshine, she bowed her

head and hunched her shoulders. With a poignancy she had not felt since early youth, she longed to go home.

She had rounded one end of the lodge from the front, watching her pale brown, sleek leather shoes with some absorption, and when a male voice sounded from above, she started violently. 'Sorry,' said Pierce from above, sounding amused. 'Do you have any idea what time it is?'

She put a hand to her thumping heart exaggeratedly, and heard him laugh deeply. Then she looked up, and found him leaning out of his open window, elbows propped on the sill, black hair tousled and gleaming glossy bright. It looked wet, as if he had just showered, and his shoulders and chest were bare. Her eyes ran over what she could see of him, involuntarily, for his skin was smooth over well-toned muscles, with just a hint of satin hair at his breast.

Then her imagination brought to her a vivid picture of the rest of him, beyond her sight and quite nude, and dark colour tinged her cheeks. To cover it, she finally explained the reason for her early rise. 'I don't sleep well in a strange bed. Besides which, I tend to be an early riser.'

'Wait a moment.' His head ducked back in, and suddenly something cream coloured and fluffy floated out the window. She lurched to grab it, and found the article of clothing to be a masculine-styled cardigan. He reappeared, and regarded her rather quizzically. 'You seem to have a peculiar helplessness when it comes to dressing adequately.'

'Unjust, unjust,' she said, without heat, as she slipped her arms into the sweater and burrowed in appreciatively. 'Last night I hadn't expected to go out on the lake, and this morning the sun looked warmer than it really is.' She sent her gaze running over him again. 'Besides, you're one to talk, hanging out of an open window with wet hair and no shirt.'

A slashing grin creased his face. She stared, obviously. 'You ought to see what I haven't on, below the windowsill.'

'I'd suspected as much.' His laughing gaze lingered on her face at that, and one brow rose slowly at her second blush.

'Is that so?' He looked to be hugely enjoying himself, and in no hurry to dress or shut the window. Then he marvelled, 'Goodness, what a high colour. It surely can't be sunburn at this hour?'

She was thankful she hadn't lost any more of her composure, as she said mildly, 'You are a horrid man, and the question doesn't deserve an answer. Thank you for the use of your cardigan. You will find it in the lake.' She started to walk away.

'I'll meet you in the dining room for coffee and breakfast in five minutes,' he called laughingly after her, and then she distinctly heard his window slam.

She nearly went. As she walked to the back, she found herself actually wanting to go. But then, apparently from nowhere, came an odd anger. A strange, shaking, upsetting anger it was, astonishing her with its force, wearying her with its inexplicability. She was angry at Pierce, she was angry at herself, but most of all, she was angry at Roxanne, of all people, for persuading her to come this weekend.

She bent at random, and picked up a twig, and then she strolled to the end of the pier and sat, leaning against an end post. About ten minutes later, Pierce found her there, staring broodingly into the water and breaking off bits of the twig to toss out. She heard him come out of the lodge, it was so quiet, and her face set into expressionlessness when his footsteps first sounded on the pier's boards.

He came to stand beside her silently. She could see out of the corner of her eye the lean, lower part of his leg, and the tip of his shoe. After a moment, when she refused to look up or acknowledge his presence as she flung her pieces of bark into the lake, he said quite casually, 'Our first date, and you've stood me up. Not a very auspicious beginning.' He squatted beside her, and then said, 'Here.'

She turned her head. He held two cups of coffee, steaming hot and suddenly pungent as the aroma hit her. 'Thank you,' she said, taking one from him. She refused to let her gaze linger on him too long, and so after a quickly flicked glance, she turned back to the water. He was lean and elegant in grey slacks and sweater. Suddenly mocking, she continued, 'Besides, I don't remember saying I'd show.'

'Is that why you're out here?' He sounded idle, bored, as though she'd done a petty thing, and she was fiercely glad she didn't care.

'No,' she told him flippantly, and sipped daintily from her cup. 'I just couldn't make up my mind whether I would or not, that's all.'

'I don't believe you.'

It was several seconds before she realised he had said that without any mockery, amusement, or anything else that would detract from the quiet impact of the simple words. When it finally registered, she was angrier than ever. He wasn't supposed to have reacted that way. He was supposed to either be amused or confused, either attracted or repulsed, and she could have felt a safe contempt for him. 'Well,' she said then, thrusting to her feet. 'You should. I have a terrible time making my mind up about anything.' She looked down at his upturned, self-contained expression, and added drily, 'Everybody knows that of me, sooner or later.'

Caprice turned to walk away, escape. He looked away, over the calm, mirror-smooth lake, and then said softly, as though he'd never seen her exit bid, as though they were having a leisurely conversation, 'You see, everyone has a basic reason for doing something. Sometimes, with the more twisted or fanatic mind, you need to search deeper for the reason, but it's always there, deep, underlying actions and thought like the still waters under the surface of this lake.'

He had caught her as effectively as if he'd reached out his large, slender hand and curled his fingers around her ankle. She felt an inner lurch, and then was frightened. Foolish, foolish, for this man was a stranger and he didn't matter any more than the others mattered. She shouldn't fear him. He didn't know her, couldn't know her. She was glittering brightness, she was cool fire, she was laughter and gaiety, and malicious gentleness, she was Caprice. Underneath that, she was untouchable.

Laughter bubbled up from her throat. She bent and set her half empty cup down carefully, and then danced away from Pierce. He swivelled, then stood, as she whirled back to face him tauntingly. 'I!' she cried, extravagantly, bowing to him from the waist, one hand held gracefully curved outward. 'I don't need a reason for doing something. I do it because I want to, like a spoiled child.' She pirouetted lightly, silver blonde hair flying. Then she faced him again, mockingly. 'In short, I know myself for what I am. I am a social butterfly! I flit from place to place! I flirt, hook the fish, reel them in bit by bit, and let go of the line when I grow bored! I have fun. I do what I wish. Finis!'

She bowed again. Laughing applause from behind her, and she turned to find Jeffrey, Lane, Roxanne and Gwynne treating her performance like a huge joke. She threw open her arms, and laughed again, calling out, 'My sweet public! My audience!'

'Come on in, you nut!' Jeffrey called back, his pique of last night a thing of the past, almost forgotten already. 'Breakfast is hot and ready!'

She glanced back at Pierce, who looked indolent, hands in his pockets and head tilted back as he looked at her with a half curled, lazy smile. She did not like that smile. 'Nice show,' he told her, sardonically. She blew him a kiss, and thankfully ran away. Just as she reached the others, she remembered her coffee, by now probably quite cold and abandoned on the pier, but for the life of her she wouldn't go back to get it. He brought it out. He could take care of it. She didn't care.

Behind her, unheard, Pierce repeated conversationally, 'But I still don't believe you.' Then he bent and picked up the cups, and went back to the lodge also.

Inside, she followed the others to the large, tasteful dining room where several hot dishes had been set on the sideboard. As each began to compile a breakfast, Caprice found a silent presence at her elbow. Pierce handed her cup to her, which she took without a word and drained. Then she refilled it at the sideboard, and sat at the table, unobtrusively putting distance between herself and Pierce.

'What, no breakfast?' Jeffrey teased, as he sat beside her.

Too aware of Pierce's presence, too aware of his aloofness from the others and his idle contemplation of herself, Caprice turned to Jeffrey and replied, with a careless flick of her finger to his collar, 'That's right, love. And do you know why?'

'No, why?' His eyes devoured her, and she saw Roxanne out of the corner of her eye, a bit pale.

'Because I'm playing tennis with you after breakfast,' she told Jeffrey, letting her eyes go wide as she stared into his. She licked her parted lips, and saw him swallow. 'And do you know what?'

'What?' he whispered. Everyone was watching them, avidly.

She found herself looking to Pierce. He was frowning slightly at her as though she were an alien species that he couldn't quite identify. Then she looked back to Jeffrey and told him sweetly, 'I'm going to win.'

Emory, who had just come into the room, laughed.

She looked into sunlight, letting it blind her for a full moment to make her dry eyes water. Then, with her head bowed, she rubbed at them with thumb and forefinger for they stung. She looked across the court at Jeffrey, who was stretching lazily while he waited. Full of confidence, he had eaten a large breakfast while teasing her unmercifully. She had responded with warmth, in an attempt to demonstrate to Pierce that she was indeed the flirt she'd claimed to be. It had apparently worked, almost too well. Roxanne wasn't speaking much to her, and while every one of the guests was present to watch the match, Pierce wasn't. Life could be, she reflected sighingly, almost excruciatingly predictable.

'Ready?' she shouted enthusiastically to Jeffrey, who threw her a mock salute. The tennis court was privately owned by the Langstons, and somewhat secluded from the lodge by a row of pine trees, though still visible.

He had given her the first serve, and, as they positioned themselves in the appropriate corners, everyone settled at the sidelines. 'Go get 'im!' called Emory, as he sprawled in the grass.

'Piece of cake!' She turned to smile sweetly at Jeffrey, and then turned sideways. A graceful, leisurely throw of the tennis ball up into the air, her borrowed racquet coming up with a snake-like quickness, and both her feet left the ground with the force of that first blow. Jeffrey never saw the ball pass him.

Nor did he see the second ace she slammed over the net. Emory looked ridiculous, with his mouth hanging open, and Roxanne had finally come out of the sulks, laughing until she had to hold her sides. Astonished and rather furious, Jeffrey pulled together quite nicely, but he had been thrown off stride from the beginning, and she never let him regain control, making him run for every one of his returns.

She couldn't blame him for being amazed at her ferocious playing. She was rather pleasantly surprised herself. But the running, pivoting, sheer hot work of it felt good to her. It was as if she were exorcising her own private devil, instead of plastering Jeffrey all over the court, which she granted was probably the case.

At the end, she laughingly told her chagrined opponent, 'You ate too much for breakfast! The same thing happened to me last week after lunch. Don't feel bad, you probably could have creamed me.'

Jeffrey mopped his sweaty brow and glanced, askance, at the now empty court behind them while the others hooted at him in good-natured derision. 'Somehow,' he replied, with a quick heaved breath, 'I don't think so.'

Caprice was hot and breathless herself, but still

feisty, so she rounded on Emory with a predatory leer, remarking conversationally, 'As I recall, at breakfast you laughed at me.' He began to protest volubly as she took Jeffrey's racquet and tossed it to him, handle upright.

'Come on, Emory!' Petra coaxed.

'Put your money where your mouth is!' Roxanne taunted.

Amidst his excuses, Caprice smiled dangerously. 'That's all right,' she said gently. 'You don't have to play if you're afraid to.'

That did it. Emory marched to the court with his jaw squared, while Jeffrey threw himself on to the grass to watch with glee. This time first serve was determined by a flip of a coin, and Caprice lost. As she took her standard receiving position at one end, half crouched for a sprint in an unpredictable direction, out of the corner of her eye she saw a dark, elegant, strolling masculine figure coming their way.

His first serve, she sent into the net. His second, she returned decently enough, but lost the volley, and soon the game. All the while, she was terribly, totally, tensely aware of that aloof, watching shadow under the pines.

Sunshine beating down on her head, lungs working hard, feeling the muscles in her thighs tremble, she held the ball for a moment, bending over at the waist while she took a breather. Silence, from the sides and the other end of the court. *Go away.* The ball thrown, her body arched into sleek motion, coming down to the asphalt with both feet planted, feeling the jar of it all through her body. Emory lost the volley.

Quit looking at me, damn you. They switched sides. Her side hurt her, and she pressed her hand deep into the flesh under her ribs. And she was mad. This time, however, it was mostly directed at her own stupid reaction to someone she barely knew, but it had the same vitalising effect as it had on her first match, and she proceeded to send Emory into agony with a diabolic finesse. He was too fleshy, too heavy to be really quick at short, intense spurts, and he, too, had eaten a hearty breakfast, so it was really to no one's surprise that she carried that match, too.

Afterwards, Emory was ribbed as much as Jeffrey had been, while Caprice stood in silence and held her hands up to her forehead, panting. 'You OK?' Roxanne asked quietly, and she nodded without expending energy to speak back.

She could suddenly feel Pierce's approach with every part of her blood-pounding, hot body. Jeffrey turned to her, then, and said, 'Hey, you know who you really need to play is Pierce, here. He'd be a good challenge for you.'

She pressed her hand to her side, feeling soreness where she'd had the stitch. 'No.'

Pierce had been saying something to Gwynne, his head bent to her, black hair and dark eyes, and white, white smile. Jeffrey, with a typical obtuseness, ignored or didn't hear her short reply, and turned to his older brother. 'Wouldn't you like to play Caprice? I'll bet she just might be able to beat even you. What do you say, want to make a date of it tomorrow morning?'

'I won't play with him,' she said, quiet and

still. Was it her imagination, or was there more significance to that statement than she'd meant to give it? Pierce looked at her. Their eyes met. An awkward silence fell over the group.

That still expression, that mature, mobile body, those liquid sparkling eyes, that proudly held, proudly moulded head. She felt the blood leave her face, going quite pale under her tan, which left her eyes peculiarly large. He had expected no different, she could see. She made herself grin weakly, as she offered a tension smoother. 'After all, I came here to vacation, not to train.'

A few smiled back, while Jeffrey, ever ignorant of deeper undercurrents, laughed. Pierce didn't say a thing, nor did he react in any discernible way. Just those eyes, in dispassionate, clinical observation of her heat-streaked, taut face.

She whirled away, feeling, for no clear reason, hunted, and she threw over her shoulder, 'I'm going to shower! Tickets for sale at the box office!'

She left them laughing, every time.

After supper, Caprice lounged on a window seat, effectively taking up enough of the space so that no one offered to join her. The group was in the family room, and behind her, Jeffrey and Roxanne were playing a disjointed, ill-ruled billiard game while Petra and Emory made themselves scarce outside, and Lane, Ralph, and Gwynne played records and drank wine as they sprawled on couch and armchairs.

The afternoon had been idled away. Caprice, who had pleaded exhaustion after the tennis from that morning, had lounged in a garden recliner while the males, with Roxanne and Petra, played touch football. Gwynne kept her company and they had talked while watching the others frolic laughingly on the green, smooth lawn. For touch football, they ended in tackles a surprisingly large amount of the time, though the young men took care not to hurt either of the girls.

Pierce had disappeared, and had not been present at the evening meal, which had been more formal than Friday's. She told herself she was glad and very nearly believed it. Certainly she did not feel herself to be under any tension, but the evening had a flat quality to it that she could not quite explain to herself.

Ah, well. Tomorrow evening, and it was home again, home again, jigitty jog. The childhood phrase made her smile.

She roused herself and whipped the rest into a game of charades, which somehow became imbued with a hilarity that made the rest of the downstairs echo from their laughter. Towards the end of the evening, she wandered out of the family room and into another, shadowed room, and she searched the wall for a light switch, curious to find what the room contained. It was a library, amazingly well stocked, she found, and she wandered through it, lightly browsing.

As she reached a section almost wholly consisting of philosophy, both modern and classic, Jeffrey spoke from behind. 'Those are Pierce's. What's more, he's read them all, if you can believe it.'

She turned, with a smile. 'Didn't you read philosophy in college?'

'I'm still waiting for the movie,' he said drily. He took a step forward, and became serious, too serious. 'Caprice——'

At the same moment, she whirled away, and broke through to say animatedly, 'This is such a lovely place! I must remember to thank your parents for so graciously hosting this weekend party. They're nice, I like them.'

'Caprice——' he began again, more strongly.

'And do you happen to know if Roxanne has gone upstairs, yet?' she asked lightly, with a quick, neat turn of her head to meet his eyes. He wasn't that obtuse, and his smooth skin darkened.

'No. She's in the family room with the others,' he replied shortly.

Her eyes ungentle, her voice soft, she suggested, 'Then I think we'd better join them, don't you? Petra and Emory were so boringly obvious.'

For a moment she thought he would balk, but good breeding and manners won, and he backed from the door to let her precede him into the hall.

But in the family room, she bid them all a light and lilting good night, for she'd had quite enough. All she wanted was the privacy of her strange bed upstairs and to wake in the morning, knowing that she was leaving that day.

Mr and Mrs Langston had left for the evening, and the upstairs hall was shadowed and dark. Her lavender dress slid cool and smooth against her legs as she strode for her door, already envisaging herself slipping between bed sheets, lying her head down on soft pillow.

A noise behind her, and a bare split second later Pierce said quietly, 'And good evening to you.'

She froze dead still and wished him gone. But then a neat pivot on her high heel told that he was still there, coming down the hall, shadowed like he'd been last night. She replied, with finality, 'Good night.'

He came too close. She felt a thrill of recognition at the faint whiff of aftershave. 'What?' he said, even lower. 'So soon? It's early yet.'

'But then I was up early, and played strenuous tennis,' she pointed out, longing to back up a step but refusing to make that revealing move.

'Oh, yes. This morning. What an energetic performance you gave.' His lifted hand, moving to touch at the hair of her temple, was feather light. She couldn't think why it shuddered through her. She used all manner of light caresses, especially with the opposite sex, as in straightening a tie, touching the cheek, that sort of thing. They didn't mean a thing, and yet seemed to help ensnare the man's attention, and she could now well understand why. 'You were angry this morning, for some reason,' Pierce said, his voice a mere rumble in his chest. 'I haven't figured out why.'

'Angry?' she whispered. 'Nonsense! You've a terrific imagination. Don't look for hidden motives that simply aren't there. You will be disappointed.'

'I don't know why you bother,' he said then, tapping her chin gently with his forefinger, rhythmically. 'I don't know why you play the charade. I don't understand, and I don't have to, but I will tell you this. Jeffrey, the others, I can see through like glass. You and your anger, and what goads you to your actions, I cannot fathom. That tells me louder than anything how different you are.'

Now he was lightly rubbing the backs of his fingers up and down the side of her neck, and she pulled back with a jerk. Then she bent her head, and ran her fingers through her hair, furious at how they shook. She snapped, 'You don't know what you're talking about! For God's sake, this is a ridiculous conversation.'

'You're angry again. What an intriguing emotion to be wasting on such a ridiculous conversation. I might almost think I've hit too close to home.'

'Damn you,' she said, barely audible, abandoning all social light-heartedness.

'No, really,' Pierce insisted, and now she could clearly hear the smile in his voice as he shifted closer. 'If not that, tell me. Is it that you're angry at how you shivered when I did this against the side of your neck?' His hand, touching warm and soft at her pulse point.

She turned and confronted him, as an animal at bay will, and, with a light tinkling laugh which almost convinced even her, she fitted her hand to the back of his head, feeling silken hair and bone structure, and then she gently propelled him down to press a kiss to his lips, hers softly open. For a moment, he held perfectly, even rigidly still. She had a fleeting impression of his body pressed along hers, and then she stepped back and cocked her head to one side.

'I don't know,' she told him, consideringly, devastatingly. 'Not anything to shiver or get angry about that I can see. Good night.'

She turned to go.

But he wasn't devastated, as many younger men had been by her almost contemptuous dismissal from time to time. It had always been a good weapon held in reserve: crush them when they became too pressing and uncomfortable, and they never came back.

At least, before now. Now she was dealing out of her league, which she'd known all along. Now she was dealing with a mature, intelligent man, who thought quickly, was more secure, who reached out and grabbed her by the wrist to yank her laughingly back. She fell into his arms, one of which snaked around her waist and hauled her hard against him, one of which curved around her shoulders. She didn't even see his head as it plummeted.

CHAPTER FOUR

BUT she felt his mouth drop down hard on hers, she felt that just fine. And she felt his lips open as he drove deep, pressing her entire body length, from top, to slim hips, to legs, against his taller, slightly curved torso. Through her dress, she felt his slim belt and body heat. Her hands curled into the material of shirt at his shoulders, as her head fell back, and warmth flooded her.

He took his time as he took her lips, leisurely, with a concentrated, enthusiastic thoroughness. The sheer sensuality of it had her longing to respond, but she wouldn't, she wouldn't, not to him, not this man, not to this. The force of her conflicting impulses sent a deep tremor through her.

He lifted his head. Through the dimness, she saw him smile, and she knew he must have felt the shiver also. 'Good night, Caprice,' said Pierce, serenely, and he let her go to walk down the hall.

Furious, shaking, she watched him leave, and then came to life, bolting into her room and slamming the door shut behind her. What was even more infuriating was that she was reacting just exactly how he wished her to, and she kicked viciously at the end of her bed with a muttered, 'Damn it!'

It did not help her feel better.

When she slept, she dreamt strange and disconnected images with the recurrent theme of entrapment threading through them. When she awoke, she lay for several minutes, thinking over the dreams and puzzling over their meaning. Her body warmth had made a snug cocoon between the sheets, and she was reluctant to move and disturb that. But finally her muscles protested, and she arose, to shower and dress quickly, and consider how she was to keep herself busy until the others emerged from their bedrooms.

Avoid uncomfortable situations at all cost. Yes, she should keep busy doing that. It was her cardinal rule, especially involving relationships. But somehow Pierce, either by chance or design, managed to burrow under her skin, and he kept burrowing until it hurt. For God's sake, they'd only danced together, rowed on a smelly lake, and shared a kiss. Or really, she supposed, it had been two. But, these days, any self-respecting eighteen-year-old should be able to handle that sort of thing, and she was no teenager, nor was she inept at dealing with people.

Or manipulating them. A rather tired feeling, one that had nothing to do with time of day or length of her sleep, descended on her. That was the crux of the problem. She was used to being the master manipulator, and having the ability to attract or repel people, according to the situation and her mood. It was not necessarily a bad trait, for she rarely used it for reasons other than her own comfort, but the problem was, Pierce refused to be manipulated. He did not go away on command, nor did he put a halt to his penetrating observations simply for her pleasure.

What an awful man he was. She had at first been attracted to him, but she was thankful she was no longer, for now she knew better.

Feeling much lighter at heart, she left her room and skipped down the stairs lightly, looking around her as she couldn't decide what to do with herself. Perhaps the library? She could pick out a light novel, and then move to the family room to listen to music while she read. But no, she felt too restless for that, and who wanted to read when the sun was shining so brightly outside?

Sounds from the library, someone approaching, and somehow, somehow she just knew who it was going to be. A wild feeling, close to panic, came over her and she nearly bolted for the front door, but it was too late. She would not give him such a view of her, scrabbling to escape. Instead, she turned to smile coolly as Emory came into the hall.

Almost, she let surprise show ridiculously on her face, but he wouldn't have been in any state to notice it, anyway. Deep lines of exhaustion were cut into his face, and he looked older, discouraged; curiously, heart wrenchingly; not at all the puppy-dog personality she'd always attributed to him.

'Good heavens, man,' she said quietly, shocked out of all social frivolity as she walked towards him. 'What's happened to you?'

'Hm? Oh, good morning, Caprice,' he replied, a heaviness in his voice which was unusual. He looked around him, as if seeing everything for the first time. 'I—couldn't sleep.'

She regarded him sharply, frowningly, and
then jerked her head towards the library. 'Why
don't you tell me about it?'

He followed her back into the room and, as she
turned to stare at him questioningly, he strolled
over to the large windows comprising most of the
far wall, staring out, his blond head gleaming a
pale gold in the reflected sunlight. He looked as if
he would like to speak, and then just bowed and
shook his head.

'Come on, Emory,' she urged in a low voice. 'If
you'd like to talk, feel free. I don't gossip, nor do
I break confidences.'

He glanced back at her, his good-natured blue
eyes dark. 'I proposed to Petra last night, and she
refused,' he said simply.

She blinked once or twice, and tried to fit what
he'd said into the framework of what she had
observed of the pair. Petra had shown as much
sincere interest in Emory as he had for her. 'I
find that a bit hard to believe,' she said finally,
and she sat in an armchair, crossing her legs. 'I
could have sworn she was in love with you.'

'I'd thought so.' His face shook, and she felt
suddenly appalled. This was was not a man with
a sadly bruised ego, or a disappointed heart. This
man was shattered.

'Emory,' she said, as gently as she could.
'Come sit down.' He sat, leaning forward and
staring down at his hands, laced and hung
between his knees. 'Now listen. Several people
have noticed you and Petra this weekend. Even I,
who hadn't met her before, could see that you
two must have some sort of history together. And

I've noticed how she would look at you. If someone else has noticed, then it can't be your imagination. That girl does care for you.'

'Then why?' he whispered to his hands. 'Why did she say no?'

'I suppose,' she replied drily, 'you didn't think to ask? No, I can see you didn't. I don't know; who can say what went through her mind? Perhaps she was simply afraid of the thought of marriage. God knows, it's a serious commitment.'

'I have a steady, well paying career. I don't smoke, rarely drink and never heavily, and my family has an excellent background. I—I'm a gentle man,' he said. 'How could she be afraid?'

'You'll never know, unless you ask her,' she said, leaning forward to touch at his hands. He looked up, and into her dark violet eyes. She smiled faintly. 'Take your time, get your courage up and your composure back, and then talk to her about it. Ask her to explain. It might have been nothing more than that she simply needed to hear what you would say if she refused you. Since apparently you didn't even question her reply, she may now be as shattered as you are.'

A hope was born in his eyes, and grew. 'Do you really think that's it?'

She shook her head. 'I don't know. Someone once told me, though, that we never do something without a reason. I didn't say this to him, but he was right. It's just that sometimes we don't know the reason ourselves.'

She didn't know why, but she looked up and to her right. In the doorway, Pierce stood leaning against the doorpost, hands in pockets, making the material stretch tightly over lean hips, feet crossed. He appeared as though he had been listening for some time, face quiet, without a smile.

She was shocked, immensely so, and feeling vulnerable. But Emory was talking then, and she had to drag her eyes back to him. 'You've made me feel tremendously better,' he told her, gratitude sincere in his eyes. 'I think I'll go upstairs to shower and change. Maybe if I can bring myself to it, I'll talk to Petra later today.'

Caprice touched him again, lightly. 'Let me know what happens.'

He stood, and bent to press a kiss to her cheek. 'Thank you. I will.' Then he turned to the doorway, and she was able to risk another glance in that direction. It was empty, for Pierce was already gone.

Or at least she'd thought he was gone. When she followed Emory into the hall, feeling an absurd relief that Pierce had had enough sensibility to make himself scarce, she found that he had merely backed up in the hall and was walking towards them again, as if having just come down the stairs.

Emory saw him first and said to the older man, 'Oh, good morning, Pierce. Nice day.' He turned to Caprice, and his expression softened. She gave him a small smile back, and he touched at her arm before running up the stairs to his room.

Pierce and she were left looking at each other, silently. He was in deep burgundy red slacks, with the cream cardigan she'd borrowed yesterday over a pale rose shirt. In it he appeared darker

than ever, and for the second time she noticed the
beginning of lines which were carving themselves
on either side of his thin nostrils.

'Oh,' she said, deliberately offhand, eyes wary
and pebble flat. 'Good morning, Pierce.' She
turned to walk away.

He fell into step beside her, a slight smile
beginning at the corners of his mouth. 'Nice day.
Running away again?'

She lurched to a stop, and refused to look at
him as she said between set teeth, 'What do you
want?'

She felt, rather than saw him shrug. 'Did I say
I wanted anything?' he asked, limpidly. Then, as
she refused to look at him, he said quite seriously,
'I didn't mean to overhear. You were obviously
sharing something confidential with Emory.'

'You made no quick effort to get away, I
noticed,' she said, with a snap. They entered the
dining room, which was empty.

'I'm only human.' That, with another careless
shrug.

A quick turn of her head, and she stared at
him. 'What does that mean?'

He went to the other end of the dining room,
pushed open a dark panelled swinging door, and
said cheerfully, 'Good morning, Mrs Vandusen.
Would coffee for two be any trouble this early?
Thanks.' Feeling left on a dangling end, she
wandered around the table, touching chairs
lightly with her hand. If she'd thought she could
get away with it, she would leave him right then
and there, but that, even for her, would be too
appallingly rude. No, that's not true, she realised,

as soon as she'd thought it. She felt a curious desire to thrash out the rest of the conversation with him.

He turned back, neatly. She knew, suddenly, that he wouldn't answer her question. People always had a limit to how far they would open, in social circumstances. God knows, she certainly did.

'I meant,' he said quietly, strolling to the table, 'that I had come to the doorway at a very enlightening moment and, since I wanted to hear more, I waited.' His eyes met, and held hers, dark diamond bright. 'No excuse.'

He drew out a chair for her courteously, large, slim hands curling around the edges of its back, and hers were the eyes to fall first. She sat, head bowed, and he then took a seat directly to her left, just around the corner of the end of the table, his knee brushing hers. She was intensely aware of him so close, and held herself tight because of it.

'Here you are!' said Mrs Vandusen smilingly, as she backed through the swinging door, laden with a tray. 'Shall I set it on the sideboard, or would you like it on the table?'

'The table's fine, thank you,' replied Pierce, and the housekeeper set down the things close to him, and then poured.

'Would either of you like breakfast?' the older lady then asked.

Caprice, who had been watching silently, reached for her offered cup and declined with a smile. After letting her reply first, Pierce shook his head, and the housekeeper left.

She stared into her cup, fine bone china, and concentrated on sitting very still. His eyes ran over her slowly, and she could almost feel it as a physical touch. A muscle bunched in her jaw, a quick pulsing reflex.

'What an enigma you are,' he said then, leaning forward to put his elbows on the dark grained wood. 'Contradictory, sympathetic, light-hearted, angry, inconstant. Unfathomable, when you choose. Shall I hazard a guess?'

'Would I be able to stop you?' she asked mockingly, though not unkindly. She sent a fleeting glance at him, and found him smiling at her, dark head angled.

He didn't bother to answer that. 'I think,' he said softly, and she nearly jumped out of her skin when she felt a finger touch delicately at her rigid jaw. 'I think that you're fully aware that I find you very attractive. And I also think that you're attracted to me.' The finger traced down her neck. She turned her face away and stared blindly across the room. 'And far from the mindless unreliability you seem to wish to convey, I believe you're motivated by a whole complex rash of reasoning I can only guess at. There's a deep person in that lovely body, underneath all those layers. It's just a matter of finding her.'

That muscle in her jaw was not rigid. It was trembling, and she turned to stare into Pierce's eyes. 'How amusing,' she said, and was shocked at herself for, instead of it coming out lightly as she'd intended, the words, and her face, were stark.

His eyes quickened. His hand then went under

her shirt collar to cup the nape of her neck. She told herself she should want to draw back, but her head felt heavy, willing to be propelled to him as he leaned forward and kissed her with gentle, open lips. Her eyelids fell.

Neither heard the sounds of people approaching. Caprice felt as though she were falling deep into the sensation of his warm, curved lips and the coffee scent within his mouth. There was a noise at the open doorway. She saw Pierce draw back, and then turn his head to look, quite calmly. In turn, she knew he must have seen the startled, shaken awareness that she felt quiver over her features, but she could not control it.

She deliberately took an extra second, forcing herself under control while Pierce exchanged greetings with his mother, Jeffrey, and Roxanne. Then she turned very blandly and smiled at the three, noting the various reactions of rage, jealousy, and sheer, simple consternation.

Later that morning, after the others were downstairs, an idle discussion was held as to how they would spend their time until the first of them had to leave that afternoon. Pierce had excused himself from the dining room with a quiet word, and a strange look at Caprice. Jeffrey was ignoring her for the moment, and Roxanne acted thoughtful and withdrawn. Why life had to be so unnecessarily complicated, she wearily did not know.

Quite soon, the possibility of swimming was brought up for, as Ralph put it, though the weekend had been balmy, today it was actually quite hot. Caprice kept silent, with a rather set

expression, as the others quickly and enthusiastically agreed that a swim in the lake would be nice,
and so it was settled. With a wry twist of her
mouth, she looked at Roxanne, who suddenly
looked quite understanding, for the brunette was
the only one who knew her well enough to be
aware of her aversion to deep water.

The group tramped upstairs to change into
swimsuits if they had brought one, or to borrow
one from Jeffrey, as the family kept several in
various sizes for just such an occasion. Roxanne
stopped Caprice just outside her door.

'Look, you don't have to swim if you don't
want.'

She smiled at her friend, feeling warmed. 'I
don't mind, really. I don't have to go out over my
head if I don't like, and can adequately paddle
around in the shallow water. Besides, it'll feel
good.'

'Well,' Roxanne said, wavering. 'You should
have said something.'

'And make a big deal over something stupid
when everyone else wanted to? No, thank you.'
Caprice pushed open her door, and with a
flashing smile threw over her shoulder, 'Beat you
downstairs!'

But she didn't, for she took the time to braid
her silver blonde hair to keep it out of her eyes,
and consequently was the last outside. The heat,
magnified by the concrete path, hit her bare arms
and legs pleasantly, and she had to slit her eyes
against the sun's bright glare. The boats were all
to one side of the pier, which left the other side
and the end free for diving off. The others were

already in the water, several attempting to play volley ball, while Ralph clambered out to launch powerfully into a somersault dive off the pier's end. She winced as he hit the water with a skin-splitting slap, to surface laughingly.

But what caught and held her attention, sending an odd shiver down her spine, was the sight of Pierce, who had apparently come out directly after leaving the dining room. He was off to one side in a lounge chair, black hair gleaming wet and slicked from his strong forehead, naked torso gleaming gold and sleek, narrowing to slim hips encased in brief, dark blue trunks. He was reading through some papers, with a folder lying on the grass beside him, aloof from the others. Her gaze skittered down his long, lean legs, muscular and masculinely shapely, and then she determinedly ignored him as she walked with every appearance of calm to the lake's edge.

Body sleek and lusciously tanned in her borrowed black one-piece swimsuit, she walked gracefully and sedately into the water until it reached her chest, and then she launched into a leisurely dog paddle. Emory greeted her with such warmth that Petra looked briefly stricken, and Caprice could have kicked him. But in the next instant she started to smile and, as it certainly couldn't hurt his cause any if Petra were made just a bit jealous, she responded with a low, intimate reply, and a brilliant laughing glance.

After several minutes, holding herself aloof from the rougher water play, she decided she had put in a respectable showing and turned to make back for shore.

Jeffrey called out, laughingly but with an edge in his voice that had not been present before that morning, 'Don't tell us you're leaving the water already, Caprice? You haven't even got your hair wet.'

The others took no notice, but his voice had carried over the water. She saw fleetingly that Pierce had raised his dark head. Roxanne turned her head sharply. After a moment, she said, with every appearance of normality, 'I don't feel like washing my hair later, that's all.'

She looked at Jeffrey. He gave her a glittering smile. 'Pierce doesn't like to be disturbed when he's working,' he said, with soft maliciousness.

She looked as surprised as she felt, for, paddling around in the water and concentrating on keeping her smile on her face, she hadn't even thought of Pierce. Then a flashing anger lent a cutting edge to her voice as she said, 'Grow up, Jeffrey.'

She turned back to shore, her toes sinking lightly into the silken sand, which, with the water lapping under her breasts, was comfortably within reach. Behind her, she heard an odd, angry little laugh, and then a small splash.

A sharp, urgent shout of warning from Roxanne shocked her. 'Cap, look out! Quick——'

In that instant she knew a sheer, unadulterated terror bolt through her. In that instant, too late, she launched for shore, managing only a strangled, 'God!'

In that instant, too late, she felt two hands, like horrible manacles, fasten around her slim ankles, and she was yanked under the surface before she had time to draw in a sobbing breath. The last thing she heard as the water closed over her head was Roxanne's furious shout.

Dead silence, dead silence, roaring blood in her ears, no breath. She fought convulsively, in deep panic, but the water hampered her movements and he was far too strong. Nightmare seclusion, no air, thrashing limbs and a dark terror numbing her mind. Black death, no breath, oppressive water bearing her down, dead silence, paralysing, paralysing.

She fought herself as much as he, knowing eternity as a torment. *Don't fight. Don't panic.* God, she was panicking. She tried, one last time, to push back that overwhelming, mind robbing terror. *Phobias are irrational.* But it was too late, the eternity had caught up with her, and so had the terror, swamping her mind like the water had swamped her body, black and total, black and total; she knew she was drowning, she knew despair. A sob broke from her snarling, panic-rigid lips, and water filled her mouth. Perhaps five, certainly not ten, seconds had passed. She curled tight, and motionless.

But then movement exploded under the water, that motionless, death-filled tomb that rotted at her strength and took away her reason. The manacles at her ankles abruptly loosed her, but she couldn't move her locked, trembling limbs and felt herself drift. Another sob, and she swallowed water the wrong way, immediately retching, swallowing more, seeing dancing spots behind her eyelids as a true unconscious blackness roared at her like an oncoming train.

Her head broke water at the same moment as hard, compelling hands snatched at her. Open, blinking eyes seeing nothing but streaming wetness and golden brown skin. Her head bent to the water, mouth open; she tried to breathe, tried to retch, coming out with a strangled, choking sound. Her shoulders, under the impersonal hands, convulsed as she weakly tried to sob. Then the sounds hit her of Roxanne screaming at Jeffrey, in a rage, 'You damned idiot! You stupid jerk!'

Through it all, Jeffrey said, stunned and blank, 'What's wrong with her? What happened?'

She couldn't move her limbs, couldn't do anything but shake horribly and loathe the water so dangerously near, so ready to suck her down. Then Pierce said, directly in front of her and shocked to a whisper, 'My God.' Blinking her eyes to clear them of the water, all she could do was stare at him, uncomprehending and blank, eyes black and immense, face pinched, teeth chattering. Everyone else watched, appalled.

Pierce drew her close, and bent his head. Where had he come from? Her fingers clutched bruisingly at his upper arms. He pushed her face to his bare chest, and she tried to say something, but all that came out was a terrified whimper. Her rigid body was flush to his, and his arms went around her tightly. He murmured in her ear, soothingly.

But what she heard the loudest was Roxanne's retort to Jeffrey. 'She can't stand having her head under water, genius! For God's sake, why couldn't you act your age, and leave her be!'

Pierce said to her quietly, 'Now calm down, sweetheart. It's over, all over.' The fear began to recede, like low tide. But when he loosened his arms a bit, she convulsively jerked, drawing her legs up as her fingers raised welts on his skin. He appeared to be quite unaware. 'I'm not going to let you go. Don't worry, I've no intention of letting you loose until we're at least out of the water.'

The others couldn't hear what he was saying in her ear, but they could see her distress. Roxanne asked, voice hushed, 'Cap, are you OK?'

Tightly, voice catching, she gulped, 'Fine. Be OK in a second.'

'I didn't know,' Jeffrey said. 'I'm sorry.'

Pierce sent a look over her head to his younger brother, eyes like black steel. After that, he ignored Jeffrey totally, and began to walk slowly out of the water with her. She heard Emory say, uncomfortably, 'Uh, anything we can do?'

Pierce said, common-sensible, 'We're going to sit in the sun for a little while. She'll feel better when she's warmer.' His utterly calm manner eased the atmosphere considerably, and he was rewarded by her muscles unclenching. He turned her in his arms, until she was facing away from the others, and as he felt her legs slowly, sluggishly begin to take her weight, he withdrew one arm, keeping the other tight and secure around her waist. Her head was turned to him, cheek pressed against his shoulder. The others saw his head bend until his cheek rested on her wet hair.

Coming out of the water was hard, for her legs

felt ridiculously weak, and her body felt heavier in comparison to the buoyancy from swimming. They went slow and easy, her thigh muscles quivering, and when they had reached his lounge chair, he pushed her unresistingly into it, and then draped a large beach towel over her shoulders. She shivered as though she had a high fever, and he came down beside her to take her into his arms.

From time to time, the now subdued group in the water glanced their way but could only guess at the low conversation being held, her head ducked low, Pierce's head quite near. Jeffrey was the target of many accusing glances and looked more miserable than Roxanne had ever seen him.

At the lounge chair, after a long silence when warmth finally began to creep back into her chilled limbs, Caprice said, soft and bitter, 'I feel like a fool.'

His hand went to the back of her neck, rubbing gently at the tense muscles. 'I don't think I've ever seen such terror as I saw on your face when you broke the surface. You can't dictate to emotions or fears.' She turned her head away. Pierce touched at her braid, then moved his hand to slide it up and down her shoulder bracingly. His bare thigh was pressed hard on hers, and his greater body heat seared her skin. She wished she could get closer to him and that marvellous warmth.

'I couldn't think,' she whispered. 'I couldn't breathe.'

His voice was gentle. 'How long have you been that way?'

'All my life, isn't it stupid? I've tried to overcome it, even tried to jump off a diving board once. I got out to the end of it, and couldn't move. My brother had to pull me off again. It's dumb and irrational.' She rocked forward, and put her head on her knee. 'It takes over my mind, and I just—freeze.'

She turned her face to one side, and while he continued to stroke at her back, she began to feel relaxed and very tired. Her eyes fell on a scattered pile of papers on the grass, and then she remembered. 'Weren't you sitting here, before?'

He replied drily, 'Yes, until I heard you give a kind of strangled croak, and saw how real Roxanne's worry was. Nobody else seemed to know what was happening, except Roxanne and I, of course, so I dived in and grabbed a handful of Jeff's hair to yank him back. He let go, I came up, and you popped up like a floating ice cube, doubled over and unmoving. I must admit, that gave me a bad turn. For a moment, I thought you'd gone unconscious.'

'I almost had. I'd started to black out when you grabbed me.' Unexpectedly, she started to cry. He bent over her curved back, and she felt the weight and warmth of him as he pressed his lips to the nape of her neck.

'Ssh. Come on now, it was bad, but it was only for a few seconds, and now it's all over with. Dry your tears. We'll go inside and you can shower and get dressed, all right?'

'All right. I just feel so mortified.'

'Sit up and look at me.' She did, and his eyes were stern, his face hard. 'Stop it. Do you hear?

Phobias are something out of a person's control. You couldn't help it. If Jeff hadn't acted like the fool he is, it wouldn't have happened. Are you ready to go indoors?'

She remembered his work, and looked at the papers. 'You don't have to come with me. I'm all right.'

'I want to,' he said, and that was all there was to it.

CHAPTER FIVE

PIERCE saw her to her room, after they had walked into the house slowly, his arm still tightly about her shoulders. When she had shut her bedroom door behind him, she sagged against it with her legs trembling in delayed reaction. Then she dragged herself weakly to her tiny bathroom to shower, wash her hair and, afterwards, dress.

Her face was still too pale, and her eyes strangely blank, when she checked her appearance before going back downstairs. Pierce had told her he would wait for her in the library after he had dressed, also, and so she rather listlessly supposed she should go on down. All her energy seemed sapped, and she felt much more like taking a nap.

As she descended the stairs, she found herself thinking rather distantly how odd it was for her to feel such terror at one type of water, when, say for instance, a shower, with water cascading over her head, didn't bother her in the slightest. A shudder went through her entire body. One was so deep, and the other so safely shallow . . .

Voices sounded in an incomprehensible murmur from the family room, and, as she checked briefly in the library and found no one there, she headed towards the back of the house.

She could identify Pierce and Mrs Langston long before she could distinguish words, and quickened her pace.

'. . . You weren't out there, you couldn't see her face. She was in absolute terror,' Pierce was snapping impatiently. In automatic reflex, her steps lagged, and she felt acutely uncomfortable to be overhearing two people discussing her.

'All right, maybe she didn't put on an act. Maybe I misjudged,' said Mrs Langston. Caprice felt an acute shock. 'After all, I saw it from the back window and, God knows, I didn't understand what was going on. But you must admit, darling, you have been paying her an awful lot of attention, and we all saw you both this morning.'

'Drop it, I'm warning you,' Pierce said, his voice going silken.

'But I can't! Just let me say this one thing, please! She's an inconsistent butterfly, all colour and no direction. Why, she's got Jeffrey, that dear boy, Emory, and now you after her, and after just one weekend!'

'You don't know what you're talking about,' he said harshly.

'Oh, I don't doubt she's a lovely person! That's not the point. But you're so different, Pierce! You're older, mature, you're responsible and steadfast.'

'This is a ridiculous conversation.'

Angry. What an intriguing emotion to be wasting.

'My dear, I never try to run your life, you know that. Heavens, you're too old, and far too strong a personality for that. But I couldn't help but say this. You'd just find yourself weary of her in a little while, or she would weary of you, and one of you would get hurt.'

'Have I suggested a deep and intimate relationship between us, yet?' Now exasperation. Caprice found that she was clasping her hands together so hard, they hurt. 'We should end this. She'll be down any moment.'

'You're complete opposites.'

'Don't you think I know that?' His sigh.

She backed away noiselessly, suddenly ashamed to find herself caught by the same weakness Pierce had confessed just that morning, and when she was safely away so that neither would hear normal footsteps, she walked to the library and sank into one of the armchairs and bowed her head.

Everything Mrs Langston had said was true. Everything, and she had known it all along. It had been the underlying reason why she'd tried to avoid him after that first evening of dancing under golden hung lanterns. What could he possibly see in her after a while? Her life was indeed shallow and she had lived it too long, for she didn't know how to change. She'd been taught her lifestyle since she was a small girl, and had to truthfully admit she loved the parties and the outings, and light chatter. If she yearned for something else, why, didn't everyone yearn for something different, even in the most ideal of lives?

A senseless, useless, ceaseless attraction for a man she barely knew, and she was suddenly unhappy with everything. She would just hold on until she got home. Her perspective would change then. She didn't know enough about Pierce to have founded anything lasting or concrete—she didn't even know his main interests in life, his goals, his dreams, his hobbies. She knew nothing about him, except for the look in his eyes, the low laugh in his voice, the feel of his arms, and the sight of his naked chest. A mere infatuation!

The last thing she wanted was to hurt, or be hurt. It had gone on far enough. No. That first, mocking kiss of hers had been too, too far.

Pierce said from the doorway, 'How are you feeling?'

Fine and dandy, yessir. A slight smile to him, and she said, 'I'm much better. Feeling silly and a little tired.' The smile faded, leaving her looking somehow older.

He walked forward, slowly. Light grey slacks this time, and a short-sleeved matching shirt. His eyes were on her, sharply. 'Is anything wrong?' he asked. 'You look—odd.'

She shook her head a bit absently.

'Would you like something to drink?' He sat in the armchair opposite her, the same that Emory had occupied that morning.

'No, thank you.' Her reply was distant, scrupulously polite. There was certainly nothing to suggest the utterly humbled and crushed emotion she'd experienced when hearing herself discussed so disparagingly. But, oh, no doubt she was a lovely person. Something tight lay, leaden, in her chest.

Pierce was frowning, his mouth held thin as he took a slow and deliberate assessment of her.

'Something is wrong. Still dwelling on earlier? You shouldn't be.'

Swift anger. 'You don't know me. Don't make assumptions.'

Astonishment, then a darkening anger of his own. 'In case you'd totally missed the point,' he said bitingly. 'I'm trying to be thoughtful, and to see that you're all right after having a nasty shock.'

She lifted her eyes from her hands clasped in her lap, a sudden, queerly stern glare. 'You want to help? Then don't push, don't pry at me, and don't make conjectures about my possible state of being!'

He held himself quite still, an elegant man, with quick-moving, quick-assessing eyes. His expression had changed after the astonishment and fleeting anger to settle into hardened lines of remoteness. At the look, she strangely wanted to cry, for all she could think of was the gentle, comforting touch of his lips against the back of her neck. 'My goodness,' he said, slow and sardonic. 'Anything else you'd like to add to that?'

Her elbow leaning on one arm of the chair, she put her head down and rubbed at her eyes. 'That seems,' she replied wearily, 'to be quite comprehensible.' She wished she could feel hostile to him, but all she could feel was regret.

Mrs Vandusen said from the doorway, 'Pierce, you have a phone call. Would you like to take it here, or upstairs?'

He raised a dark brow at her, and said, with a causticity that made the housekeeper raise her own in sharp surprise, 'An inadequate end.'

Caprice rose from her chair. 'But so appropriate. Don't bother going upstairs.' She smiled without humour. 'It's far easier for me to leave.'

Outside the library, she heard his voice, already so familiar, and it changed from abruptness to a far more businesslike tone. She bowed her head, put on her happy face, and went outside.

The others were just climbing out and drying off with a pile of towels which had been laid close by the pier. When she approached, there was a moment of awkward silence, as everyone tried to think how they would say what they were feeling. Then Jeffrey met her eyes, which were calm and smiling. There was true mortification in his glance. 'Look, I'm sorry——' he began.

She laughed and, feeling sorry for his hangdog look, she walked over to snake her arm around his slim waist for a brief, tight hug. 'Don't be more stupid than you can help, hm?' she said, and pressed her lips to his cheek to take the sting out of her words. 'You weren't to know I don't like getting my head under water! For heaven's sake, forget it!'

After that, she moved away, and acted so utterly normal and carefree that everyone else relaxed with a collective sigh, and soon the atmosphere was light-hearted once more.

Lunch was a laughing affair, and Caprice was much relieved to find Roxanne being warmer to her. Soon after the meal, she found an occasion to ask the brunette if they could leave fairly soon, and raised a blonde eyebrow at the other girl's apparent eagerness to be gone. The weekend had not turned out like either had expected it to.

So it was that, when Lane finally mentioned that he would have to be leaving, both Caprice and Roxanne were quick to add that they, too, should be departing. They would rather drive in full daylight; Roxanne had an early appointment the next morning; of course they would much rather stay; it had been a lovely weekend, too bad it had to end. But Jeffrey understood, didn't he? Of course he did, so they would just pop upstairs to get their things.

She parted with Roxanne in the hall, entering the room that had been hers for a few days without bothering to shut the door. As she was a tidy person by nature, repacking her suitcase took a matter of minutes, and she soon went to her tiny bathroom to make sure she hadn't forgot anything before going back down. She walked in, pivoted on her heel and was out again, almost in the same motion. Then she stopped, as abruptly as running into a wall.

Pierce leaned casually against the side of the door, letting his dark gaze roam the bedroom before settling on her tense, still face. He had apparently been out, either walking or driving with his window down, for his black hair was blown out of its sleek style, whipped back. 'Heard you were leaving,' was his laconic opener.

She forced herself to walk calmly to her suitcase which was lying open on her bed. With a snap, it was closed, and she pressed the twin catches with her thumbs. The double snick was abnormally loud in the room. 'I heard a rumour to that effect,' she said, surprising herself by the sarcasm evident in her voice.

'Was that supposed to be funny?' He was still angry with her. She could feel it, sense it almost as she would see a physical colour, a dark hazy red. Did she transmit her anger as clearly as he, was that how he'd intuited it so accurately yesterday? Or, more disturbingly, were they that sensitive to each other?

'No,' she said slowly. 'It was stupid.' Though her back was to him, she knew he had relaxed somewhat. She asked shortly, 'What do you want?'

'To say goodbye, what else?' Now it was his turn to mock. What was that strange ache she felt?

'So, goodbye.' Insolent, repelling.

'Oh, no.' His low laugh, sounding briefly, still angrily. 'You're not getting off that easily.'

Her head jerked up and around in startlement. 'What is that supposed to——' she began. But she lost the thread of her question; indeed, she lost all remembrance of it, as Pierce thrust away from the doorpost, strode her way, and pulled her by the shoulders right to him.

Too surprised to react, she met his chest with a distinct jar. A golden chest, sleek and sun-kissed smooth, flexing muscles and warm against her cheek, with sweet-smelling air filling her nostrils instead of filthy lakewater. Her shiver and his steadiness. Hand holding arms.

Hard, and snaking around her once again while she reacted sluggishly, slowly, far, far too slowly, and she knew it even as his hand slid under her

hair to tilt back her head. His lips. Which
touched her nape with a lost gentleness, lost, as
anything possible between them was, too different, too different, man and woman, warm body to
warm body. Mouth to mouth, tongue to tongue,
unexpected. So unexpected, in fact, that she was
intensely shocked. Not by his open mouth,
moving hard and urgent on hers, which in turn
was feverishly eager on his. No, she wasn't
shocked by the kiss, she'd been kissed far too
many times for that type of reaction. She was
shocked by her own response to it, deep and
heartfelt, acutely and passionately aware of the
hard muscles in his clenched thighs, the heartbeat
she felt pounding in a roar against her own
breast, his bent head, those long, moving fingers.
Something uncontrolled in her loins leapt surging,
and it scared her half to death.

Not in control.

He raised his head slowly, reluctantly. Through
blurred vision, she could see his own blind shock,
and knew that he was experiencing the same
jarring emotion that she had. He stared down at
her for a full pulsing moment, eyes dilated. Then,
without a word, he released her and walked out
the door.

She stared at the empty rectangle, feeling a
deep, bone-weakening tremble in her limbs.
Then she turned her head to one side, whispering
quietly, 'Damn you.' What it meant, not even she
knew.

Roxanne found her a few minutes later, sitting
on the edge of the bed quite still, staring towards
the floor at her feet, her face a white blank. The

brunette's voice was subdued as she asked, 'Are you ready to go?'

'What?' Caprice said tiredly. She looked up, and then her eyes really focused, and expression came back to her face, though not colour. 'Oh yes. Of course.' She calmly reached for the handle of her suitcase, and followed her friend down the stairs.

Goodbyes and thanks were effusively made. Caprice felt the weary lies even as she mouthed them with a smile on her pale lips, but knew of no other way to get through it. She spoke a few words with Mrs Langston, that poised, attractive lady, and in her eyes was a dry knowledge, which brought a disconcerted frown to the other woman.

Then there was the moment when Caprice was turning to Emory and hugging him affectionately, regardless of the interested, speculating look of the others. She stood on tiptoe to whisper into his ear, 'I want to hear how things turn out between you and Petra. Let me know, all right?'

She drew back, and he smiled down at her. 'All right. Drive carefully, you two.'

'We will,' promised Roxanne, while Caprice caught a frank glare from Petra. She smiled, positively sunny in the face of the other girl's ill-concealed hatred.

Though she was terrible at reading maps, she held routes well in her memory, and had to consult Roxanne for directions only a few times on their way back. Their drive up had been nice, as the sun had been shining, but on their return Caprice found the sun so fierce, she had to resort

to dark glasses to combat a headache and the
bright glare.

'Cap,' said Roxanne in a small voice, when
they had been travelling for some time.

After a moment, stifling a sigh, she grunted,
'Mmm.'

'Are you glad you went?'

How should she answer that? She was too tired
for any dissembling. 'No,' she said.

'Neither am I.' A long pause. Wind whistled at
the speed of their passage, a constant, high,
inhuman sound. 'Cappy. Why did you agree to
come?'

She licked dry lips, and immediately gave it up,
for the wind whipped them dry again instantly. 'I
didn't want you hurt.'

'Jeffrey.' Roxanne's voice was flat.

'He's an unreliable fool, and wholly likeable.
But I wouldn't count on devotion from him.'

She could sense the other girl's dark head
jerking to stare at her. 'I don't—really know you
at all, do I?'

She said quite gently, 'No. But I shouldn't get
worked up over it, if I were you. I don't think I
know myself very well, either.'

Roxanne said, quick and sudden, 'I think I'm
glad I went after all. I kept getting mad at you
every time Jeffrey would pay attention to you
instead of me. But after this morning, I can't—
like him as much as I did.'

'He wasn't to know that I'd get so upset,'
reminded Caprice.

'No, but anyone could see that you weren't
eager to horse around. Even Ralph said that you

were so careful in the water, he hadn't the heart to splash water at you. And instead of respecting that, Jeffrey acted pettily. I was very angry at him.'

She shot her friend a smiling glance. 'It wasn't hard to tell.'

She could almost hear Roxanne's mind working, wheels grinding busily away. They had known each other for a long time, but somehow totally open conversations had been rare between them, and Caprice rather felt that they were embarking on a new and fragile beginning. The brunette tried another leading remark. 'Petra is furious with you, did you notice?'

She couldn't resist the totally wicked grin that brought her face to unexpected animation. 'Well,' she said composedly, increasing the car's speed as they neared the Virginia state line, 'she shouldn't have refused Emory's proposal, then, if she's going to get so worked up about it.'

'You sly devil! Is that what's going on, then?' Roxanne was warming to her more and more.

'Yes, but Emory's quite innocent of it. He's just grateful I let him pour out all his woes on my sympathetic shoulder. His perspective is not exactly, well, penetrating. I can't wait to see what happens!'

Her friend laughed, and strangely sobered again, quickly. 'Cap,' said Roxanne for a third time, and it was the most hesitant of all. 'I—came to your room, and found you with Pierce. I left and came back again, since I didn't want to disturb you.'

Dear heaven. A dark colour tinged her cheeks,

a swift, jaw-clenched reaction. Roxanne wouldn't have disturbed her unduly. Pierce had been the one to completely destroy her composure. 'Forget what you saw,' she said, from stiff lips. 'It was nothing.'

'It looked like a lot more than nothing to me,' Roxanne retorted.

'I said forget it.'

'You fell for him.'

'Let's change the conversation.' They were nearing the other girl's home, thank God.

'But anyone could see it. And he was attracted to you, too. What's wrong with that? He seems like a gorgeous man; you always have the luck. And I've never seen you so seriously interested in someone like that. You should keep in contact with him.'

From a warm, relaxed sharing, to this sudden, shaking discomposure. Couldn't the other girl see how this was upsetting her? She tightened her trembling fingers on the steering wheel until the bone showed white through the skin at her knuckles. 'It was nothing,' she repeated, like a litany. 'He's not my type. Now please, Roxanne, just drop it!'

They pulled on to the street where the brunette lived. 'All right,' Caprice heard her say, clearly confused. She pulled into the driveway, and came to a stop near the front door. The silence between them drew out until she turned her blonde head to stare at the other girl, who was steadily studying what could be seen of her face behind the dark glasses. 'I still don't know you very well, do I?'

Her lips trembled, obviously. With a quick gesture, she touched Roxanne's shoulder, and then turned her face away. The other girl's goodbye was gentle.

Caprice pulled into her own driveway twenty minutes later with the haggard feeling that she had survived a war. Wearily she dragged out her suitcase, and made her way inside the house. The late afternoon led her to suspect that she would find things very quiet, and she was right. After letting Liz know she was back, she went to her room, dropped her suitcase uncaringly to the floor, locked her door behind her and stripped. A hard yank had her bedcovers tugged back, and she crept between her sheets with a deep, shuddering sigh. The day had been incredibly draining, and she concentrated single-mindedly on falling asleep as quickly and easily as she possibly could.

Thum, THUM, thum, thum, THUM, went the beat of her heart in the silence of the dark murky waters; all she could think of, and all she could hear, was the beat of her heart going thum, THUM—wait a minute. This wasn't a dream. She rolled over, knuckling groggily at her eyes, and shouted, 'What?'

Ricky's voice resonated through the wood. 'You're late for supper. Did you want any?'

She emitted something between a groan and a whimper, and briefly stuck her head under her pillows and tried to think. She wasn't hungry, but if she didn't get up now, she'd never sleep the night through. 'I'll be down in a minute,' she mumbled to her sheet.

'Did you say something?'

'I said I'll be down in a minute!' That, irately.

She heard him laugh. 'Well, you didn't need to shout.'

Dragging herself out of bed was possibly one of the hardest things she'd ever done, but a quick cold splash of water dispelled the grogginess, and she slipped on a fresh set of clothes with the neat economy of a student well used to calculating such early morning routines down to a second. After a few strokes at her hair with her brush, she slipped out of her bedroom and ran lightly down to the dining room, supper, and her family.

'Sorry,' she said to her mother, who intensely disliked tardiness. She fell into her customary seat, smiled a bit wanly at her father, and looked without much interest at the serving dishes. Horrors, there was creamed corn.

'Liz fixed you a salad,' said Irene, to her daughter's disgusted shudder.

'I'd better get it.' She started to slide back to her feet.

'No need, sweetie.' The housekeeper came around from behind her, set the salad by her plate, along with her favourite dressing. She smiled her thanks as Liz winked at her, and then left.

'Yeow!' Ricky uttered, wincing extravagantly as he looked at her.

Irene looked weary. 'Is that noise really necessary?'

Her son ignored her, and leaned forward on both elbows. 'That must have been some party,' he observed. 'I could trip and disappear into those shadows under your eyes. Hangover?'

'Your sympathy overwhelms me,' she said to him drily. 'But as it happens, no. I just got a headache driving today, that's all.'

Her father subjected her to a silent, piercing scrutiny while he thoughtfully chewed. He reached for his water glass to drink before asking laconically, 'Have a good time?'

She pulled a face. 'Should I lie?'

'Good heavens,' said her mother, touching a napkin delicately to her red lips. 'Whatever went wrong?'

'Nothing,' replied Caprice tersely. Everything. Unexplainable. She bent her blonde head to her salad, and concentrated on an even distribution of the Italian dressing, fully aware of her mother's exasperated glance.

Irene pressed. 'There must have been something wrong. Why, everyone knows that the Langstons' hospitality is superb! Who chaperoned?'

'Mr and Mrs Langston. Look, the weekend went as well as could be expected—I just didn't enjoy myself, that's all. I was bored!'

'Meet the older son?' asked her father, idly.

She felt a strange, unexpected leap in her chest, and swallowed past something in her throat. 'Yes. Look, do we have to talk about this now? I'm still groggy from my nap.'

Irene paused in eating and looked at her. 'For God's sake, why so reticent about it? Come on, tell us a little about what you did, who you met. Is the older boy as handsome as they say?'

Caprice took a deep breath, staring down at the salad she didn't want, feeling all urge to eat it fade away. She pushed it away from her. 'He's no boy. I didn't scream when I looked at him the first time. All we did was dance, play tennis, and swim. The weather was nice. Jeffrey was not.' Her head angled sideways, sending a hard angry glare to her mother. 'Would you like to know when I went to bed last night, too?'

Irene drew in a swift breath. Then, furiously, 'Young lady, there's no cause for such abominable behaviour. If you can't be civil to your own family, then I suggest you leave until you can.'

'Irene,' said Richard, a low aside. 'She's tired.'

'It doesn't matter,' said Caprice in brittle tones. She stood. 'I didn't want supper anyway.' Ricky raised his dark head to stare after her as she swiftly exited.

She made straight for the den, where a small, yet well-stocked bar was kept, and she mixed herself a rather careless martini, chucking in with a liberal hand several green olives from the tiny refrigerator below the counter. She loved olives, could sit and eat a small jar at one sitting, puckering in sour ecstasy the whole while. Her mother and father never had to worry about her nipping at the alcohol when she was a curious child. But they'd had a running battle to keep any olives stocked in the house.

Ricky slouched gracefully into the room, and threw himself on to the nearby couch while she sat leaning forward in an armchair, rubbing tiredly at the back of her aching neck. 'Nasty temper,' he remarked, his manner supremely disinterested. 'Unlike you.'

'Did you follow me just to tell me that?' she marvelled sarcastically, and drank at her martini.

'Oh, no. I was finished eating,' he assured her. 'You know she's going to make you apologise.'

'She can take a hike,' Caprice retorted, direct on the heels of his statement.

His head came up, and he stared at her for a few moments before saying slowly, 'That attitude is not exactly conducive to a serene home life. Are you sure you want to push principles that far?'

'Look, she's the one who pushed at me first. I didn't want to talk about it, and I made that perfectly clear.' She set her glass down on the table beside her, a sharp punctuating chink. 'If she wants to ignore my wishes, then she's going to have to expect that I'll get angry about it.'

He held up his hands. 'Hey, no argument. But you know how she hates it when we talk back to her. She's going to be in a royal brood for the rest of the week.'

She bowed her head, so tired, so tired, longing to go back to bed, knowing she shouldn't. As she closed her eyes, tears stung at the back of them, and she ran her hands through her dishevelled, fine hair. The fingers met on either side of her neck, at the nape. Pierce had kissed her there. 'If you can't speak your mind in your own home, then what kind of a home is it?' she said, bitterly. She sighed heavily, her mouth turning down, an unhappy bow. 'I'll—apologise tomorrow. I can't tonight.'

Ricky took in her huddled posture. 'You do what you think best.'

She raised her head, and grimaced at him. 'It's not fair that you and dad should put up with her brooding, just because of me.'

'Tell her that. No, on second thought, don't mention it.'

She grinned weakly. She watched as her brother sat, still regarding her with his bright eyes.

'Just one thing, though,' he said softly. She raised an enquiring eyebrow. 'What did happen, over the weekend?'

CHAPTER SIX

CAPRICE did apologise to her mother that very next morning, hiding her still present resentment, putting on a show of sunny spirits. She was good at putting on a show. Irene said a few sharp words to her bland daughter, realised how silly her pique had been, and no more was said over the subject.

As the week melted away under the scorching sun of high summer, Caprice's low spirits began to disappear. It had been a stupid mistake, that weekend. She was heartily thankful it was all over with.

The weekend promised to be dismal, and wet, with leaden grey skies looming sullenly overhead, and the weatherman forecasting dire news. Roxanne was in a gloom because it was the end of the month and, no matter how much pleading she did, her father obstinately refused to advance her the next month's allowance.

The brunette simply couldn't understand the arrangement Caprice had with her father. She had to smile whenever she thought of Roxanne's frank envy, for no amount of explanations could convince the other girl that their system would not work for the Cauleighs. She and Richard would periodically sit down together to discuss the state of her finances. Aside from a set amount already determined for the upkeep of the

Porsche, which was her responsibility, she could ask for as much money as she wished and, as long as she could present a logical reason for having it, she got it. The arrangement was based on confidentiality, for it never would have worked with Ricky either, and a mutual trust. Many times Caprice didn't request any as she couldn't see the point of asking for money when she couldn't, or didn't want to, spend it. As a consequence, for less, she ultimately got more, in the way of her father's silent respect.

All Friday morning she'd spent visiting Liz and helping in the kitchen, for she liked the other woman's sense of humour and cheerful common sense. But when the afternoon rolled around, she found herself itching to do something, and left the house for a long car drive. The wind was too cool for anything more than cracking her window open, and the dull sky seemed to suck all colour from the surrounding landscape, so that everything looked lifeless, without vitality.

For some reason, for no reason, she thought of Pierce, and she wondered what he was doing, where he was going. Who he was seeing. She shook her head, angry at herself. She had thought of him entirely too often this last week. Not a day would pass but that she let her mind wander to him.

Him. What kind of man was he, to attract her attention and hold it, without even being present? No one else had been able to prompt that in her. She loved to go out, and did quite often, with anybody and everybody who was presentable enough, and who asked. She loved men, all men: young, old, silly, wise. She could talk with them seriously and intelligently, when she chose, but she could also flirt with the best of them.

She liked how males looked at her, the caressing, admiring glances, the amusement and, sometimes, the startled respect. And she never had settled for one deep relationship, for, as she always expostulated, why pick a book when you can have the whole library to browse through?

Why, then, why did she remember Pierce's quiet words and angry voice? Why did the thought of his gentleness and his sudden passion stir her? He was just another man! Her hands slid on her steering wheel, fingers unconsciously working. She attempted to dismiss his image, but her mind was traitorous. A splendid, elegant figure of a man; an intelligent, responsible man; an exciting man. But not for her: oh, no. He wasn't her type.

Then why had it hurt so when she'd overheard someone else espouse the same sentiments? Of course; naturally, it had been her pride that was dented. She liked to think herself good enough for any man, as anyone did, and it irked her to know that someone else thought differently.

She loved to drive for long periods at a time, alone, with low music playing over her excellent car stereo. She whiled away the entire afternoon, driving towards the east coast with no definite goal in mind, then turning back towards Richmond when she began to feel tired. She had to stop for petrol, stretching her legs once she was out of the driver's seat and suddenly longing to be going somewhere, really going somewhere, with a destination and a goal, and an ending.

But she was merely going home. As she pulled into the wide, spacious drive, she noted the sleek, dark Jaguar tucked into the parking space that shot off the main asphalt strip, leaving passage free to the garage. As she pulled into her garage space, she mentally ran over the families whom she knew to have such a model. There were perhaps four she could name off the top of her head, but none with the right colour. Of course, the Langstons owned one that particular hue, but Jeffrey drove a convertible. She frowned, puzzled. Could Mr and Mrs Langston have come for a visit?

She checked her watch. Almost six, and the evening meal was at seven. Whoever it was must have been invited to stay.

She looked down at her slim legs, encased in skin-tight, faded jeans, with diminutive Nike tennis shoes beneath. She was a mess, and Mrs Langston always appeared to be coolly elegant. She would slip in the back way, sneak upstairs to wash and change, and then come down to make her appearance.

Through the kitchen, and lightly stepping in the hall, she managed to escape detection. With the long length of stairs ahead of her, she prepared to leap up them quickly when Ricky appeared in the hall, whistling tunelessly. He caught sight of her, and strolled her way.

'Hiyah,' he said.

'Ssh! I don't want Mother to know I'm here until I've had a chance to clean up,' she whispered, and then she stared at him, for he was wearing a peculiar smile. 'Who is it? The only

family I could think of who owns that colour
Jaguar is the Langstons—is it Mr and Mrs
Langston, or both?'

'Oh, Mr Langston,' said Ricky cheerfully.
'Come on, move it or lose it. I'm headed upstairs,
myself.'

She still didn't get it, even after his odd
smile and that rather devilish twinkle at the
back of his eyes. She was too preoccupied with
wondering why Jeffrey's father had come, and
could make no sense of it. Not even once did
she guess the truth, as she quickly showered
and slipped on a pale mauve dress which had
tiny thin silver stripes running vertically and
slimmed her figure even more. Silver sleek
pumps, and three thin silver necklaces com-
pleted the outfit and, after touching up her
make-up and brushing her hair, she slipped
back downstairs.

Only as she strode easily for the den did her
own stupidity crash in on her, making her face
quiver with the shock of it, making her steps
falter and then stop as she heard the unmistakable
nuances of Pierce replying to her mother's light
chatter. Later, the only reason that she could
think why she had simply not considered him as a
possibility, however remote she might have
thought it to be, was because he never commuted
to Virginia to visit the family. It was one of the
principle reasons why she'd never met him before
that last weekend.

Recovering sluggishly, she slowly approached
the small, private room the family invariably met
in before supper, and rounded the corner.

He sat on the couch, dressed as usual with casual elegance in black slacks and blazer, with pale blue sweater underneath. His dark head had been turned attentively to Irene, whose eyes were avidly eating him up as she talked. They both looked up at her entrance, Pierce's expression unreadable as he gave her a meaningless, flashing white smile, her mother's expression full of enjoyment.

'Good heavens, Pierce, whatever are you doing here?' Caprice asked composedly, her churning emotions calling that composure a lie. She let her lips pull into a slight, cool, answering smile before she turned to her mother. 'Hallo. Is Dad home yet?'

'No, dear,' replied Irene, rather impatient with the small talk. 'Pierce stopped by to see you and, as you were out, I invited him to stay for supper. Where did you go?'

She broke out of that immobility that had held her fixed to one spot in the room, making smoothly for the bar. 'I went for a drive. Tell me, Pierce, isn't it rather unusual for you to come south for the weekend?'

'Yes,' he replied, speaking for the first time. His voice shivered into her, and she nearly dropped her glass. 'Usually I go to the lodge when I wish to get out of New York. It's much more quiet.'

Caprice splashed gin into her glass carelessly, and then tonic. She forgot to add her favourite twist of lime or to stir it, so when she sipped at it some moments later, the drink tasted terrible. She then turned, and casually leaned back against the counter, gently swirling her glass.

Irene said gaily, 'He's been telling me all about his work in the family business! It's so fascinating.' Her dark violet eyes widened at that, almost imperceptibly. Her mother was never fascinated by business in her life.

A quickly shot glance to Pierce, who was quite relaxed with one arm along the arm of the couch, showed that he held a faint, but unmistakable, gleam of amusement in his eyes. Then he was looking at her, hard and flashing bright, and their eyes met with an almost audible clash. She wiped hers free of expression and let her gaze wander blankly away.

Then Ricky entered the room, nodding to Pierce pleasantly, responding to Irene's cheerfully warbled greeting, smiling a bit secretively to Caprice. By the time Richard had arrived home from work, changed and joined them, it was nearly seven.

Unsure of Pierce's motives for being in Virginia, let alone at her own home, she retreated into an aloof silence, determined not to give him any encouragement. Of course, she was angry that he had come. Never mind that the candles, lit and burning in subdued elegance on the supper table, looked sparkling and brilliant and reminded her oddly of golden hung lanterns. Never mind that she had her ear tuned for everything he had to say, whether it was directed at her, or one of her family. Never mind that the delicately flavoured salmon nestled in thin-shaved almond slices tasted like sawdust, all her senses attuned and leaping at the dark lean man opposite her at the table.

She felt every thoughtful, searching look of his, dark eyes reflecting the flickering light of the candles. She remembered vividly his scent, which clung close and light to his body. She remembered every mannerism of his expressive hands, recalling each as he made them, astonished that she had noticed that much of him from last weekend. The expressions he wore, the quick-changing mouth, that mobile left eyebrow, the maturity of his features; she greeted them all like old friends.

She was in big, big trouble.

She was also quite aware that each of her family were sending her assessing glances in varying shades of speculation. At least her father and Ricky were discreet about it, but Irene had a terrible habit of glancing from Pierce, to her, back to Pierce again, in the most obvious way.

Irene, growing impatient with Caprice's continuing silence, said archly to their quiet guest, 'You know, when Caprice got back from New England last weekend, she wouldn't say a thing about what happened to her. We're all dying to hear about it.'

In an agony of distaste for her mother's obvious coyness, she carefully set aside her utensils, put her elbows on the table, and rested her chin on her folded hands. Beyond her sight and to her left, Ricky closed his eyes briefly and shook his head. Richard was frowningly silent.

Unable to refrain from seeing how Pierce reacted to her mother, she glanced up, eyes hard, and met his dark gaze resting on her. He looked gentle, which shocked her more than anything else would have, and then he turned to Irene and answered, scrupulously polite, 'Perhaps Caprice didn't speak of it because she had such an unpleasant time. Our lodge is by a lake. She—had a bit of an accident, and went underwater when she least expected it.'

Her mother said, in quite a different voice, 'Oh! Oh, dear. Well, she never could abide that.'

Ricky touched her knee with his right hand, under the table, and she turned to have him give her a sympathetic smile. Smoothly, Pierce was replying, 'Far from simple dislike, Mrs Hagan, she came up terrified.' He turned to Richard, then, and commented easily, 'I hear you're thinking of expansion.'

She looked quickly to her father. He just smiled. 'That's right. Who told you about it?'

Successfully the conversation turned to other things, leaving her mother momentarily nonplussed, and herself feeling quite odd. No, tell it like it is, Cap, she told herself, you're feeling grateful. At all accounts, at least he could handle her mother.

Ricky excused himself over the coffee and dessert, and it seemed soon after that her parents were making some pretext to leave them alone together, too. With a furious disgust, she thought it no better than when she had entertained her boyfriends at home when she was in high school, instead of sitting across from a fully adult, fully capable man.

She sat quite still, an unconscious remnant of her childhood days when she would hide in the most ridiculous places and think that no one could see her. Though he had been quite smooth and comfortable when keeping the conversation light, now he didn't say a thing, and the silence stretched until the atmosphere was thin and nearly unbearable.

Her screaming nerves made the slight sound of his chair scraping back almost intolerable, like nails screeching on a blackboard. She refused to look at him, struggling to keep her expression a still, calm mask.

He walked away, to the end of the room, and then back, in slow, slow footsteps. Then, with that quiet anger she'd come to know so well, he said, 'There's no need to be so acutely embarrassed, you know. Would you rather I just left?'

That had her head jerking up and her eyes widening. Only then did she realise how frustrating he, too, had found the evening. It gentled her expression into ruefulness. 'I didn't think it showed so obviously. Would you like to leave?'

He looked deep into her eyes, bending over her seated figure. 'I would like to know what you're thinking. I would like to know how you felt when you knew I was here.'

She bent her head, and put a hand to her forehead. 'I guess I'm wondering why you came over,' she admitted.

His hand came out, and she watched it with the fascination of one hypnotised. Then he touched her, warm fingers moving against the side of her face, a light and shivery caress. He whispered, 'You should be asking instead why I came to Virginia in the first place.'

She began to tremble, and closed her eyes against it, and him. 'Oh, no. Don't say it.'

His fingers turned hard, slipping under her chin and giving her a yank. 'Look at me. You asked, but you don't want to know. I left the office early, took a flight down, and drove over to see you. I want to spend the weekend with you. Are you free?'

She shoved his hand away, and stood. 'No. Go back to New York.'

'Is that what you want?' He was quite near, and not backing down. When she had stood, she'd meant to slip from him and put distance between them, but somehow got tangled into a confused desire to step towards him instead of away.

She lifted heavy eyelids to stare at him without flinching. 'Yes.' Her mouth drew tight.

Incredibly, he grinned. 'You're lying.' He drew even closer, put both hands lightly to her upper arms to coax her into leaning to him, and brought his mouth down. His whisper tickled her lips. 'You're lying through your delectable teeth.' His tongue slipped into her parted mouth to run tantalisingly over them, lightning fast.

Her mouth parted even further on a shocked gasp, and she leaped back as if stung. She brought her forefinger up, sticking it stiffly under his nose. 'Stop it. Stop it.'

Glee danced then in those sparkling eyes. He snatched at her hand, brought it near, and nipped at her fingernail with his own strong white teeth. She curled it in protest. 'Admit it. You liked it.'

'Quit teasing me.' She was horrifyingly close to tears, and cursed herself for a fool.

'But you're so painfully serious around me.

Not with anyone else, just me.' He had not let go of her hand despite her none too gentle tugs, and he bent his head, resting his cheek against her knuckles, while searching her eyes from under his brows. 'Have dinner with me tomorrow. Have breakfast, too. Let's spend the day together.'

'Go away,' she gritted, longing to say yes, knowing she shouldn't.

He let her go so fast, she blinked. 'All right,' he agreed. She felt a stupid desolation. 'On one condition. You really want me to go away, you tell me why. No lies, no prevarications, just the unvarnished truth.'

A quick, bitter twist of the lips. 'How would you know if I did?'

'I'd trust your integrity.' That shook her, and he could see it. A weary, unamused smile creased his lips.

She turned away, and looked blankly over the dining room. It stayed the same through the years, still, untouched by time. She was the one that changed. Her back to him, her head turned sideways so that she could hear his movements, she sighed. How bizarre. So few people ever asked for the truth from her. And she would give them an acceptable version, and they would be satisfied. She wondered if any of them realised the many layers of truth that existed, as many as the people populating the earth.

'I overheard you and your mother last weekend.' Yes, that was true. He was still, like unmoving stone. 'But I'd already come to the same conclusions. You and I, we're too different.'

I'm afraid of you. 'Perhaps at first we'd enjoy being with each other. But then you would want something from me that I couldn't give, or I would want it from you.' You make me feel stranger than I've ever felt before. You make me feel.

He came close, put his hands on her shoulders, fingers curving lightly, and he pulled her back to him. With his head bent, he whispered into her ear, 'Do you think people have to be alike before they can enjoy one another? If you overheard our conversation, then you must have heard my reply to her. She said we were exact opposites. I said I knew that, and it was the major reason why I was attracted to you.'

Without even realising, she laid her head back to his blue sweater. He drew in a careful breath, and one hand left her shoulder to stroke at her hair. 'I didn't hear. I must have already headed back to the library.'

'We don't have to hurt each other. We have that choice. Why don't we just take things as they come, instead of worrying so much that it cripples us? Do you want to spend the day with me, tomorrow?'

'Yes,' she whispered, and that, too, was the truth. A strange and trembling excitement filled her, as she gave into her wishes and his persuasion.

'I'll pick you up tomorrow, at seven.' He waited a moment, but she didn't or couldn't say anything. 'All right?'

'Yes.' Bare thread of sound. She felt him relax at her back, and emit a low laugh.

'Good. I'll be leaving, then. Tomorrow's going to come early.' She walked him to the front door, hearing the dissimilar sounds of their footsteps intermingling, the light tap tap of her heels with the heavier sound of his. When they reached the door, and she opened it with slow hands, she was warm and lightly flushed with the half-acknowledged hope that he would take her, hold her, open his mouth hungrily over hers and drink her dry . . .

She turned to him, and searched his dark eyes, but found nothing but a smile. The chilly wind blew over them like an invisible cloak, stirring his black hair. The air felt wet and heavy, full of rain. He bent close, saying lightly, 'See you in the morning, sweetheart.' His lips brushed her cheek.

Light and meaningless, like the first smile he'd given her that evening, soft as when he had brushed them against the nape of her neck, brief and frustrating, when all she could think of, all she could want, was the hardened, exciting feel of his lips rough on hers.

She turned her head before she knew she wanted to, and met his mouth with hers already open. A heart-thudding, still moment, and then he carefully kissed her back, measured, controlled, and pulled away. He looked odd, his face rather set, eyes full of the black outside night, and then he smiled in her general direction, muttered another good night, and lightly raced down the steps. She watched him, uncomprehendingly, as he reached the Jaguar and got in, the first heavy drops of rain splattering on his head and shoulders.

She shut the door, locked it too carefully, and then leaned against it as she stared down at the fingers which shook, showing her discomposure. No passion. No emotion in that kiss. Certainly no anger, as there had been the last time.

Gradually her leaping senses calmed, and she began to think more coolly. She found that, as she was free of his presence, so then was she free of her conviction-weakening desire to get near him, get to him, to drown in the heady feelings that were aroused whenever she was around him.

She shook her head in wonder at what he brought out in her, and then moved slowly for the den. Liz had been in the room to pick up the used glasses and wash them, so she rummaged for a clean one under the bar, set it on the counter, and then forgot about it. She leaned her elbows on the quality, glossy wood, and put her face in her hands.

She wished, achingly, that she'd had a different influence from her mother when she'd been a young child. She remembered those early days. Her mother had been a goddess, a lovely, spell-binding, fascinating parent. She remembered, wryly, how she used to perch on the counter by her parents' bathroom sink, watching Irene put on her make-up before a party. Glittering, beautiful clothes, a light tinkling laugh, effusive affection showered on her when Irene had the time, so many things impressing themselves on a young adoring person.

Caprice knew what she wanted out of life. She wanted to be just like her mother. And so she grew, watching, learning, assimilating.

She took a good, cold, calculating look at
herself. Would she be happy, doing anything
else? The answer was quick, blunt, and rather
devastating. No. She didn't want a career that
absorbed her free time, and tied her to
responsibility and commitments. She didn't want
to forsake the parties, teas, the fun and the
laughter. She liked to dress well, and she liked
other people to know it. And, fortunately, she
had a father wealthy enough to see her secure for
the rest of her life.

As she had grown older, though, she'd begun
to see her parents in a different light. Irene was as
lovely in maturity as she had been in her youth.
But Caprice also loved her father, and throughout
her teens became gradually aware that Richard
and Irene at best tolerated each other. Her
mother's glitter went just exactly skin deep;
underneath it, Irene was a shallow woman. And
Richard, hard-working, career-orientated, in-
fluential, was as different from his wife as night is
from day. They didn't understand each other. He
was heartily bored with the details in Irene's life,
as she was with his. They existed.

Caprice often wished that she had taken after
her father. She grasped business concepts, was
intelligent and quick with numbers, but she had
no more desire to work in the family business
than she would wish to work at the local car
wash. And she knew the kind of man she should
meet and fall in love with. He should be witty, a
good socialiser, charming, and interested in the
same things that she was.

He wasn't a bit like Pierce. Pierce was a lot like

her father. Pierce was responsible, quiet, deep. He was sexy, he was devastatingly attractive to her, he was dangerous. She should run screaming in the other direction.

But she wasn't. She'd agreed to see him tomorrow, and wanted to see him Sunday. She shouldn't fall for him, she knew that. One look at her parents was enough to convince her of that. But this weekend, what could one weekend hurt? She would see him, laugh with him, look at him and perhaps let herself care a little for two days. Just this one weekend. And she wouldn't see him again, after this.

Surely she could control herself that long.

She bumped the empty glass with her elbow, and remembered that she was making herself a drink. But she didn't want it any more, and tucked the glass away again as her father strolled into the den.

He sent a quick glance to her as though she were a chair, and then went to the window at the far end of the room. She knew immediately that it was all a front, and he was there purposefully to speak to her. He cleared his throat, and rocked back and forth, hands clasped behind his back. She loved him very much.

'Langston's gone, I see,' he said to the curtains.

'Yes, he left not that long ago,' she quietly replied. 'Would you like a drink?'

He did, and she poured him a brandy, his favourite after dinner liquor. 'Seems to be a good man.' She walked over to him, and gave him the snifter.

'Yes, I believe he is.'

'You seeing him?' The question was short to the point of terseness, yet she didn't take it amiss. He was interested in her life, and she appreciated it.

'This weekend I am. I—don't think there's a future in it.' She ran her eyes over her father's greying head and distinguished figure with affection.

He turned his head and looked her directly in the eye. 'Too bad. I was thinking.' He fell silent, and her attention sharpened. 'We need to sit down for a talk, you and I. It's time you had more independence. I'm going to set up an annuity for you, and stipulate its continuance in my will so that you're taken care of.'

She touched his sleeve, and rubbed up and down lightly. 'Surely there's plenty of time for that?' she murmured, disturbed by the talk.

He shrugged. 'Never know. I'm already fifty, and I'm not getting any younger. Anyway, that's not the point. Somewhere along the line, why, I guess you grew up without me knowing it.' His grey eyes met hers, and she saw his pride in her. 'Think of it. You're already twenty-two, and a fine young lady. You'll be wanting to do things, to go places, and—well, we need to sit down and have a talk.'

'I love you, Dad,' she whispered quietly.

He smiled. 'You kids have to leave some time. Sooner or later, and I know it. But it won't be the same without you around here.' His smile faded, and he briefly looked old and sad. 'Just won't be the same.'

She went up on her toes and pressed a kiss on

his cheek. He put his arms around her and
hugged her tight, and then told her good night in
a perfectly normal voice. After he left, she found
his brandy, untouched, on a nearby table.
Carefully, she poured it back in the bottle,
spilling only a few drops. Then she took the glass
to the kitchen, clean and empty as Liz had quit
for the evening, and she washed it up. She
couldn't think why her eyes blurred unexpectedly,
and made her small task impossible to see.

CHAPTER SEVEN

SHE readied herself for bed, and fell into it without much hope of sleeping, and sure enough, she tossed and turned for most of the night. As a consequence she overslept, and Liz woke her just before seven with the news that Pierce had already arrived and was waiting downstairs for her.

Feeling befuddled, she stumbled out of bed, threw on her pale blue bathrobe, and went to the head of the stairs to call softly down. Pierce immediately appeared from the direction of the den, and she saw the quick grin that slashed across his features. 'I'm sorry,' she said, pushing her tousled hair from her forehead. 'I'll be down in a few minutes. I just wanted to ask you about what I should wear.'

'Something sturdy and casual should do it, I think,' he replied, taking his time as he looked her over from head to foot. His lids drew down, making him appear lazy, indolent. 'Of course,' he added silkily, 'there's not a thing wrong with what you're wearing.'

She laughed and let her hair fall forward in an attempt to hide her blush. 'Have you had breakfast?'

'Coffee.' He was watching her, his head thrown back, with every sign of fascination.

'Liz could fix us something to eat, if you'd like.'

'Only if we can have it alone. I'm not in the mood to share you today,' he told her, with a slow smile.

'On Saturday, nobody around here shows for breakfast before nine,' she assured him with another laugh. Despite her broken sleep, she was beginning to feel positively cheerful. She started down the stairs, intending to talk to the housekeeper, but he forestalled her.

'No, you go on and get dressed. I can talk to Liz.' He waved a hand at her, and she backed willingly enough up the steps, feeling a distinct vulnerability in her night clothes. She could feel his eyes on her slim figure until she disappeared from his sight.

Rushing through her bedroom to her small bathroom, she stared at herself in the mirror for a brief, horrified moment, pressing hands against her cheeks. What a wreck she was! And she simply must wash her hair! Whirling around, she grabbed at her hairbrush, yanked it through her tangles a few times, wincing, stripped and let her clothes fall to the floor, and then jumped into the shower. Five minutes later, dripping wet, she shiveringly crept into her bedroom and drew out clothes. A glimpse outside at the overcast day had her grimacing as she dressed accordingly. Snug-fitting jeans were shaken out and then drawn over her hips. She then took a white, tailored blouse and drew that on, and pulled an oversized, bulky, light brown sweater over it. Suede, low-heeled boots, a swept up, thigh length jacket, and she was ready for just about anything.

The sound of her skipping lightly down the

stairs brought Pierce back into the hall. He walked towards her as she landed with a small, childish hop, dressed much the same as she was, in sturdy jeans, dark shoes and sweater. He looked lean and lovely, and she turned to toss her jacket into a hall chair in an attempt to hide her reaction to him.

He was behind her before she realised it, his warm hand curling around her hips and drawing her back against him. 'Hmm, hallo,' he said in her ear. She laughed, and bent her head. 'Your hair is disgustingly wet.' Long fingers drew the damp length aside, and she felt his lips behind her ear. 'You wouldn't stand me up if I invited you to breakfast, would you?'

'Not this time.' The feel of his warm lips against the chilled skin of her neck, pulled thin over the bone of her skull, sent a shiver rippling over her body, and she crossed her arms.

'That's not an entirely satisfactory answer,' he replied drily, as he let her go and stepped back. 'But it'll have to do for now. Liz has everything in the dining room, ready when you are.'

They went in to the hot, freshly cooked meal, chairs pulled close together. Caprice picked at her toast and egg thoughtfully, fully aware of his side glances from time to time, and those dark, observing eyes. She pulled a piece of toast apart, and popped a bit in her mouth. After she had swallowed, she said, 'You said something last night about preferring to go to the lodge on weekends, instead of visiting family down here?'

'That's right. I don't have a lot in common with my family, aside from business, of course.'

She sent him a quick, searching look, at which he smiled. 'Oh, there's nothing like strained relations between us, though that may change as soon as Jeffrey knows I'm seeing you.'

'I've given him no reason to hope,' she informed him, rather caustically. 'It's his own foolishness.' Pierce's expression turned dry, and she said then, contritely, 'I'm sorry. I shouldn't have said that.'

'Good God, why not?' He reached for his coffee cup, long fingers on a slim, yet powerful, hand with slight, dark hairs silken on his wrist. 'It's certainly true enough. But I do happen to find it quite understandable.'

For a moment, she didn't comprehend, and when she did, she had to turn her head rather sharply away. After finding her voice, she said quietly, 'You're no fool.'

'That remains to be seen.' A soft thread of sound, his reply.

She groped for a switch in conversation, and fell back on their previous subject. 'So you don't have much in common with your family?'

'They're quite status conscious. Climbing high on the social ladder means a great deal to them, whereas I consider it to be a waste of time,' he explained simply. There was no censure, or contempt in his voice, just a mere statement of fact.

'My mother's like that,' she said, and brooded into her coffee with an out-thrust lower lip.

'And you?' The query was light.

She looked up quickly, and stared at his guarded expression. 'I've never thought that

considering myself better than someone else
would be very admirable. I guess I don't have
enough self-esteem or arrogance.'

He reached out a careless hand and tucked a
still-damp tendril of hair behind her ear. 'I think
I'm liking you more and more,' he told her, in
tones of such surprise that she laughed aloud, in
spite of herself.

When they had finished, popped into the
kitchen very quickly to give Liz their thanks, and
shrugged on their coats, Pierce turned to her and
asked, 'So, what should we do today?'

She looked considerably startled, and had to
grope for an answer. 'I don't know. You didn't
have anything planned?'

'I meant to think of something last night, but I
fell asleep,' he mourned, eyes sparkling.

She ducked her head and looked at the points
of her boots. 'I'd suggest a drive to the coast, but
I did that yesterday. Of course, I didn't actually
go to the beaches, but I did drive in that
direction.'

'How about taking a drive to the mountains
today, then?' he asked, opening the front door. At
the gust of chilly wind that touched her cheeks
and still damp hair, she was glad to have dressed
so warmly.

She threw a smile over her shoulder at him.
'That sounds wonderful.' It didn't. It sounded
OK. It even sounded nice. But what she found
wonderful was the fact that she had the entire day
ahead of her, and she was spending it with this
man. And anything could happen tomorrow.
Two whole days, a weekend, an eternity when

there was nothing to look forward to. Two days without work, or obligations, for either of them. She savoured the thought.

He slammed the front door behind them, and put his hand, light and attentive, at her back as they strode for the Jaguar. She was pulsingly, excitingly aware of his presence beside her, so close, if she were to turn her head and look. But she didn't, and as she rounded the rear of the car his hand fell away. If she'd paused to think of it, she would have assumed that he was simply moving to the driver's side, but that thought was never carried to fruition. His hand, which had left her back, clasped her slim wrist, and as she took that one step away from him, he laughed and yanked her back.

Her whole body was whirled around, and she fell against his chest. Surprise thudded through her and immobilised her limbs for the time it took him to wrap his arms around her tightly. Then her head jerked back, and her mouth opened in a question that was never spoken. His black hair was wind-tousled, his face creased with the lines of a wicked grin, his eyes dancing with gleeful purpose. He bent his head.

And kissed her, but it didn't seem as simple as that. Oh, no, it wasn't simple at all, the way he fastened those hungry, hard lips over hers and moved them until she slanted her head sideways and kissed him back. There was a world of complexity in the range of sensations inspired by that kiss, the cold of his lips, the warm cavity within, his piercing, probing tongue, his obvious, delighted excitement.

Something sounded, deep in the back of her throat, and her knees went lax. Her bones were nothing but pure putty, her arms captured against his chest, her head falling back. He lifted his head, and ran his glittering gaze over her flushed face.

She swallowed, blinking rapidly as she re-alised that her devastation must be written all over her face. Why so enthusiastically this morning, when last night he would barely touch her? She cleared her throat, and thought that for pride's sake she might try saying something witty and intelligent, so that he could see she was still in control of herself. 'Well,' she said, and the word was faint.

'I wanted to do that last night,' he said, cocking his head as his eyes fell to her rose-flushed lips. 'But hated to think what your mother would imagine if she'd walked into the hall and saw us.'

'Oh!' was her startled reply. Then, strongly, 'Good God!'

'My sentiments exactly.' He loosed her slowly, almost reluctantly. 'Now that we have that out of the way, are you ready to go?'

She sent a sharp look his way, and found him smiling as though he were in love with the world. It sent a thrill running through her. 'I think so,' she said sedately.

After settling into the luxurious car, they drove north and east, to the Shenandoah National Park in the Blue Ridge. There they found a place to park, and wandered in relative quiet. He reached for, and received, her hand as they trudged along a well-beaten trail. The mountains, which had risen ahead of them like an incredibly huge giant, were heavy with a grey mantle of mist, obscuring places along the mountaintops. The only splashes of truly vivid colour were the wild flowers scattered plentifully as though chucked in great handfuls by the brooding giant.

They didn't meet anyone on the trail, though it was obviously well used, and perhaps the explanation for that was the continuingly greying sky, and the heavy, warning quality to the air. After having strolled in some silence, she was startled to hear him speak. 'You do realise that, if we stay out for much longer, we're liable to get wet.'

She glanced at his jacket and then at her own. Both were made of a water repellent material which nevertheless wouldn't manage to keep them completely dry. She looked about her, reluctant to give up the peaceful intimacy. 'I don't care, if you don't.'

He slanted his head sideways and squinted at the sky, and told her, 'I don't make any promises.' As she smiled, he laid his arm firmly along her shoulders, and drew her against his side, and they continued that way for some time.

But the weather was against them, and Caprice was beginning to feel tired after a while, anyway. Large splashes of water on their heads and shoulders convinced them that nature was not bluffing this time, and finally Pierce slowed to a halt, and turned her around. 'Time to head back,' he said down to her, with a sigh. 'I'm afraid we'll probably end up quite wet anyway, since we've got some way to go. We stayed too long.'

Her eyes clung to his, dark violet and deep centred black. She shook her head and smiled faintly. 'No, we didn't.'

He drew in a breath, and stepped close, his eyelids falling heavy and his head coming down sideways. She put her arms around his neck, willingly, and raised her lips to his. Gentleness; leisurely, sensual gentleness building a slow mounting blaze that no amount of rain could put out. Cold cutting wind, failing to slip between their flush, straining bodies. With her head raised and eyes shut against the softly falling rain, she was conscious only of his warmth and his nearness, his caressing mouth, while blind wetness flattened her hair to her head and made her face slippery. She raised a hand to his cheek, resting cold fingers against that lean skin and muscle, feeling the small rivulet of water which ran from his temple, down to his neck.

He lifted back his head slightly and stared down at her with widened dark eyes. Both his hands came to her face, stroking at her with fingers as wet as her face, brushing the light sodden hair from her forehead with a tenderness that made her catch her breath. She stared back, holding herself still for fear of breaking the spell of the moment, long lashes spiked with the rain.

He ran his eyes over her expression time and time again. 'We're crazy,' he muttered, the words sounding dazed. 'We're getting soaked. Come on, before one of us catches pneumonia.'

She placed her hand in the one he offered to her, and trudged along beside him. 'You don't

usually catch pneumonia, unless you're exposed
to a virus.'

'All right, all right.' His expression had changed,
was normal, teasing. 'A very bad cold, then.'

'Ugh, now you're talking.'

Even hurrying, they were a good twenty
minutes from the car, and when they reached it,
she dithered beside the open passenger door
which he held impatiently for her, mourning the
damage she might do to the upholstery until,
with an exasperated glare, he bundled her in so
fast her head spun. 'For heaven's sake, it's a car,
isn't it?' was his retort to her complaint.

They sat for some time, the heater running full
blast, and talked of light, inconsequential things.
He played with her fingers, now warm and nearly
dry. To his quiet questions, she found herself
telling him all about Ricky's scrapes, her college
days at Vassar, anything that came to mind. He
was an attentive listener, flatteringly so, for he
was quite intent, asking her searching, leading
questions which drew from her explanations
about herself that she'd once thought no one was
interested in.

'What a strange, complex, contradictory char-
acter you are,' he said after a while, in such a way
that she was quite touched. It was said with
understanding and tolerance, and held a wealth of
affection running as a strong underthread. The wet
streams of water running off the car's exterior gave
them a private intimacy, warm, cosy.

Self-consciousness made her say, laughingly,
'We've talked a lot about me, but I want to talk
about you.'

'Warm enough?' He let go of her hand and raised the back of his hand to her cheek, a lazy caress which sent her eyes to glowing.

'Fine, thanks.'

'Then why don't we get back? You can take a long, hot bath, and I can go home to shower and change. Would you like to eat out?'

His head was back against the seat, showing his lean face and throat in sharp profile, the black hair still wet and clinging to the shape of his skull. The one brow she could see slashed strongly diagonal. She thought she could gaze at him forever. 'That sounds nice,' she murmured, and yawned from the heat in the car. 'Whatever you like.'

His well-moulded lips pulled into a smile as though laughing at what she said, but he didn't explain. Instead, he told her, 'I'm not much in the mood for sharing you any more than I was this morning. Know anywhere we can go to avoid meeting people you're acquainted with?'

She thought with a slight frown of her usual dining places, while he started up the Jaguar. 'I think anywhere in Richmond that's decent will be a bit of a gamble on Saturday,' she then replied. 'If you don't mind a drive, we could go to Newport News.'

'Mmm,' was his only response for a few moments. Then, 'Yes, that may be the way to go. You wouldn't mind a late night?'

'No,' she said, and so it was settled.

Caprice dozed on the way back, curled up in her corner and oblivious of Pierce's frequent, smiling glances. After being chilled, the warmth knocked her right out until he shook her shoulder. She raised her head and peered around with a hand-covered yawn, and saw that they were back at her home. With a laugh, he brushed aside her apologies, and bent towards her for a brief, hard kiss before shooing her out of the car.

The air outside the Jaguar was even colder to her, and she shivered as she watched him reverse down the driveway and pull away with a wave of his hand.

She shuddered suddenly, right down to her toes, and ran for the front door. Inside, she strode quickly for the staircase, intent on having that bath he suggested, when Irene clicked into the hall from the den. 'Oh, there you are, dear!' she said smilingly as she hurried towards Caprice, who reluctantly stopped. When she turned to her mother, she found Irene's eyes sparkling with curiosity. 'Tell me, did you have a good time? What a handsome man Pierce is! What did you do?'

'We went to Shenandoah National Park, and got rained on,' she said, brief and dry. 'Now, if you will excuse me, I'm soaking to the skin, and want to clean up.'

Without waiting for a reply, she whirled and raced up the stairs with a feeling of escape. She burst into her room, and made for the bathroom, but on second thought, turned right around and carefully locked the door behind her. It would be like her mother to come and ask questions when all she wanted to do was relax.

When Pierce had given her that quick kiss

goodbye, he had told her he'd pick her up at five
o'clock, which left her plenty of time to herself.
She ran water so hot, at first it scalded. The
warmth crept into her bones, and she sagged
sideways in the tub, her eyelids falling shut.
When she opened her eyes again, the water had
cooled until it was tepid, and her neck ached on
one side. She leaped out, dried and put up her
hair for the evening, and began to dress.

She sheathed herself in silky black, from the
severely simple dress, to the sheer tights she
slipped on to her slim legs, and the sleek pumps
she fitted her feet into. Her plain gold chains
were her only adornment, and she spent an
inordinate amount of time on her make-up until
her eyes dominated a vibrant, glowing expression.
She took her evening wrap from her wardrobe,
checked the time and found herself quite early,
shrugged, and went downstairs for a drink.

She made herself a gin and tonic, correctly this
time, and though she sipped it slowly, she was
finished by the time it was barely ten-to-five.
Ricky came into the den, and then her mother,
and she endured their interested questions, and
her mother's ceaseless speculations, until she
checked her watch and found the time to be five-
thirty. She frowned. He had had more than
enough time to get back home and change, and
then come back. He'd dropped her off at three
that afternoon.

He was merely late. She shrugged, made
herself another drink, and prepared to leave any
moment. By six, she was genuinely alarmed, and
everyone else was, too. She had just made up her

mind to give the Langstons a call, even though she'd held off for so long as she was reluctant to talk to any of them, when the phone rang.

Even in her heels, she beat Ricky, Liz and Irene to the phone, gave herself a moment to catch her breath and to let it ring one more time (for dignity's sake), and then serenely picked it up. 'Hallo?' she said, voice unruffled.

'Caprice, this is Pierce,' was the immediate reply. He sounded terse, and tired. 'I'm sorry. I would have called you before, but there's been an accident——'

She gasped, harsh sucking breath sounding clearly audible even over the phone, and felt her knees buckle. Even as Ricky's arm snaked around her waist, she was catching herself against the table, strangling out, 'Are—are you hurt?'

'God, no!' he exclaimed. And then, 'Damn it, I'm sorry for frightening you like that. I wasn't in the accident. It happened in front of me as I was on the way to pick you up. A pick-up ran a red light, and hit another car in the intersection, which in turn spun around and hit the car behind it.'

'But you're all right?' she asked sharply. 'You weren't even hit, you said?'

'No, I'm fine. I'm at the hospital at the moment. It's been a mess. In one of the cars a mother got hurt, and the two children needed someone to look after them. The father's just come to get them, and I remembered to call you. I clean forgot.'

'Don't worry about it. I quite understand. No, really, it's all right.' Irene was gabbling in the background, and she restrained an urge to turn around and scream at her to shut up.

'I'm soaked from the knees down, I'm afraid. If you'd like, I can be there in about forty minutes, but I'll have to change.'

She checked the time. 'Do you think it's worth it?' she asked, while knowing a sinking feeling inside. 'By the time we reach Newport News, it would be eight, which isn't that late, but there is the drive back. You must be exhausted.'

'Well,' he said, hesitating. 'I'm not giving up on the evening, but perhaps we shouldn't make the drive after all.'

'We could just dine in town——' she was saying, when Irene grabbed at her sleeve and shook her so hard, she nearly lost hold of the receiver. 'Hold on a moment, please.' She turned to her mother, impatiently. 'What do you want?'

'We're all leaving for the evening, dear,' Irene said. 'If you want a quiet evening in privacy, why don't you invite him here?'

Quite surprised, and unwilling to believe in such good luck when the evening had already started badly, she turned to Ricky, who shrugged and nodded. She grinned quickly. 'Out with Larry?'

He looked pained. 'We're going to see a movie.'

'Of course. How nice.' She relented, and turned back to the receiver and the patiently waiting Pierce. 'How would you like to come over here for the evening? Mother tells me everyone's leaving, and if Liz isn't around, I'm sure I can whip up something that won't kill you.'

He laughed out loud. 'Why do I feel that I'll be taking my life into my hands? No, I take it back! You're on. Shall we try for seven then?'

'Be a bit more positive about that,' she admonished with a laugh. 'All right. Pierce? Drive carefully.'

'I always do, sweetheart. I always do.'

Not long afterwards, her parents left for the party they were attending, and, from experience, she knew they would be quite late. Ricky then left, too, after scolding her mightily for her teasing in front of Irene, who obviously hadn't suspected anything, anyway. She was left with the empty house, and the knowledge that Pierce would soon be there.

A quick trip to the kitchen found Liz still there, but preparing to leave as no one had been expecting to eat at home. When prevailed upon, she willingly helped Caprice pull together a tasty casserole, along with salad, and both soup and dessert which were left over from two nights earlier, and had been frozen for just such an occasion. Caprice then waved her out the door, promised she wouldn't leave the kitchen a disaster, and hurried to set the table before Pierce arrived.

She was just setting the finishing touches, with candles ready and dark and painstakingly set silverware and heavy cloth napkins, when the doorbell rang. She jumped, and hurried to answer it, knowing it would be Pierce, and suddenly, inexplicably, so nervous she could barely breathe. As she swung the door slowly open, revealing a wet, dark night, it sank in to her that they had the whole evening ahead of them, alone, with unlimited privacy. It suddenly seemed like a long, long time.

CHAPTER EIGHT

PIERCE leaned against the doorpost, his dark overcoat hanging carelessly open to reveal the elegant grey suit underneath. His head was cocked to one side as he looked at her, up and down, and then smiled slowly. It kicked something to life in her chest, and she stood back wordlessly to let him enter.

He looked quickly around as she shut and locked the door behind him. 'Everyone gone already?'

'Yes, we've the house to ourselves,' she replied, and stepped close behind him with her arms uplifted. 'May I take your coat?'

But even as the words were leaving her mouth, he was turning around and putting his hands at her slim waist. 'This,' he stated, with some satisfaction, 'is getting better and better. Did I tell you that you look——' His head bent, and he nuzzled his face into her neck. '. . . good enough to eat?'

Her arms were up, and she didn't know what else to do with them, so she put them around his neck and held his head to her. 'Mmm,' she murmured, and his mouth began to move on her skin. Her next words came ragged. 'No, I don't think you—mentioned it. Cut that out, I can't think. Don't let me forget the casserole, or we won't be eating.'

He laughed into her shoulder, his chest

moving, and whispered, 'I've already got my meal right here. But you might go hungry.' He let her go, and moved away.

Knowing he was regarding her with great interest, she turned her head quickly away and tried to breathe evenly. 'I'll go check on supper,' she said, intending to sound light. It came out as breathless as she felt, and she positively fled as his laugh sounded like a purr of contentment.

In the kitchen, she opened the oven door twice and peered in, without remembering what she saw either time. She cursed, viciously, and looked a third time as Pierce strolled in, minus his overcoat and suit jacket.

'Looks nice,' he said, peering over her shoulder. He sounded astonished. 'Did you make that?'

She let the oven door bang shut, and turned to slap him with the oven gloves. 'As a matter of fact, yes,' she retorted. Then she grinned. 'Liz helped me whip a meal together before she left, since it was such short notice. But, I'll have you know, I can cook perfectly well without any help!'

He threw up his hands as though truly menaced by her slight figure, and then spoiled it by laughing. 'I believe you! No need for bloodshed here; simmer down! Merciful heavens, there's even soup.' He suddenly grew serious. 'I'm sorry about this. Shall we dine out tomorrow, to make up for this evening?'

Her violet eyes turned full on him, going suddenly stricken, and she blinked rapidly a few times before staring down blankly at her hands, and the oven gloves she'd forgotten she was still holding. 'You're here, and you're fine, and strong. If you'd been just one car ahead, you'd have been in that accident.' The oven gloves twisted between her fingers. 'I don't think I'm sorry for how the evening turned out.'

His expression swiftly changed, and he bent forward to press a gentle kiss to her forehead. 'Most of all, I'm sorry that I worried you,' he said softly. Then, a quick change of subject, he asked, 'What can I do to help?'

She looked up, and ogled him in amazement. 'Do you mean you know how to cook?'

'All right, cut it out!' he expostulated, his grin doing funny things to her. 'I'm a bachelor. I know how to put plastic pouches in boiling water for my supper.'

Suddenly as comfortable with him as if he'd been her own brother, she hooted in derision as she opened the refrigerator to pull out the salad. They were soon sitting down to eat, the candles lit and throwing a flickering intimate light over the two, sending the rest of the room into murky shadow.

The soup tasted as fresh and delicious as it had that first evening, thanks to the freezer, and Caprice settled back to enjoy herself. When a brief silence fell over them, she sent several curious glances his way. The candlelight threw his eyes into shadow, an occasional dark sparkle showing through the dark slanting veil. When he looked up quickly, the impression vanished and his eyes showed clear and bright.

'What do you do in New York?' she asked,

toying with her food. 'I mean, I vaguely know what your family's business is, but I don't know what you do. Textiles, right?'

'Yes, it's rather more prominent here in Richmond than in New York, obviously. My end of the business is taking the manufactured cloths and making them into clothes.'

She couldn't resist the laugh that bubbled out. 'I can just see you, sitting cross-legged, needle in mouth, working busily away. No, I know of the Langston Fashions, but what do *you* do?'

'Well,' he said, leaning back and stretching lazily. 'I handle the business, literally. The marketing, the sales projections, the management. I guess you could say, I am the management. I'm not really that visible a person in the business. You'd be amazed at how many people associate our models with our clothing. But then, that's the reason we're paying them, of course, to be in the public eye.'

She ran her eyes over his figure, lean, elegant as he was always elegant. 'You wouldn't do badly at all, in the public eye,' she said then, and turned back to her supper.

'Perhaps.' He leaned his elbows on the table after sitting forward, and laced his fingers together. 'But that's not my style. I prefer to live more quietly. Once you're exposed to publicity, there's never an end to it.'

'Mmm. Yes, I see what you mean.' They were finished with the main course, so she rose to take the dishes and to get the dessert. When he started to stand, also, to help, she waved him back, and in the kitchen she started coffee and prepared a tray. Soon, she was walking carefully back into the dining room, poured the coffee and served the dessert, and settled back into her chair. 'Jeffrey mentioned something about you being interested in philosophy?'

'Oh, yes,' he replied, with a slight smile. 'In fact, I minored in it, in college. But it doesn't make for good conversation, in general, so I don't talk about it much.'

'A philosophical businessman,' she murmured, with a laughing glance thrown his way. 'That is a definitely intriguing combination.'

His smile was tolerant. They finished their coffee and dessert in a leisurely fashion, and when she stood to stack things on the tray, he stood, also, and no amount of persuasion would get him to sit down and relax again. In the kitchen, she found two aprons, and laughingly tied one around his lean waist, and then he did the same for her. But somehow, his hands began to wander, sliding around to her front and pulling her back against him. His head bent and he let his lips wander as much as his hands, until she was flushed and trembling.

She tried for her normal voice and found a reasonable facsimile. 'This isn't getting the dishes washed.' The last word trailed away, uncertainly.

He released her immediately, and stepped back. 'No, you're right, of course,' he said, sounding perfectly normal. That, somehow, astonished her, and she didn't know what to think, as she brushed back the light wisps falling on her forehead and then went to the sink to start hot water.

The talk trickled into a few, short comments made while they worked companionably at cleaning the mess left from the meal. Afterwards, she put the dishes away while he wandered into the den and came back again, holding two drinks. 'Gin?' he asked, as he handed one to her, and she smiled, pleased that he remembered.

They walked back to the den, where he seated himself comfortably at the couch while she walked, restless, aimless, around the room. She touched at a small table as she went by, fingers gliding over the cool, hard surface, and then she went to the window to stare out at the black wet night. It was still rather early, just after eight, and he wouldn't be leaving for a while yet. Sudden panic struck her. What should she say, what should she do, how should she feel? This was different. She didn't want it to be. She wanted it as light and as inconsequential as all her other relationships, but it wasn't; this was different, she was alone with him, with something unfamiliar throbbing inside her.

It was a temporary situation. But she was being tugged in different directions by her conflicting emotions, and she didn't know what to do. She didn't know who she was, for she was motivated by reasons that even she could only guess at.

The glass was clear, and against the dark night her reflection, and that of the room behind her, stood out sharply, a ghostly mirror. She could see Pierce's dark head turned towards her slantingly, as he studied her from under level brows. What was he doing here? What did he want?

'Want to come sit down?' he asked quietly. His

expression was unreadable in the glass, and she felt as if she was with a stranger.

Without a word, she turned and walked to the couch, slipping off her black pumps and curling comfortably close by him. He turned towards her, one leg half propped on the cushions, his arm along the back of the couch. He reached over and curled a finger into a wisp of flyaway hair at her nape. The sensation was delicate, tickling, pleasurable. She turned her head slightly towards his fingers, which then went to trace the slim line of her jaw.

'Sometimes,' he said softly, staring at her, 'Sometimes I feel that I'm getting to know you, and then you can seem so distant. There's an unreachable quality about you, something always held back.'

She closed her eyes. The myriad, conflicting emotions that she had been experiencing were melding into one. That feel of his fingers cool against her warm skin. Yes, she recognised that. She turned even further and pressed her lips against them, then rubbed her cheek lightly up and down. She heard his intake of breath, and then he carefully took away her drink and set it aside.

The one emotion she then felt was a simple, wordless desire to be held and touched, kissed and stroked and caressed. When he turned back to gather her gently close, she willingly settled her head against his shoulder and turned her face to his neck. It was good, as good as every other time he had held her, and yet new. There must, she thought hazily, be as many different ways to hold

a person as there are different moods. She
pressed her lips to his neck, and opened them.

And it was somehow the same as the other
times. His body went taut, and the hand behind
her head grew hard. He bent his head, and
nuzzled roughly at the hair at her temple. The
sameness, underlying previous anger, shock, even
the gentleness during that walk in the rain; and it
was passion.

The fingers of his hand thrust into her
carefully constructed chignon and tugged it loose.
The silver blonde fluff fell to her shoulders, and
he buried both fists into it, pulling back her head
and staring for a brief, throbbing moment at her
parted lips. His head fell down to her swiftly,
mouth working on hers in eagerness. Her hands
splayed wide on his chest, feeling his warmth
through his shirt.

The soothing touch of lips against her nape, in
sun-blinded distress. The hardened ravishment,
as he took her by surprise before she left. The
coldness of his fingers as he stroked her
streaming face, upturned and still. The whirling
memories melded into the present; the smoul-
dering blaze already begun leapt to flaming
brightness. A wave of hotness rushed through
her, making her tremble. He slipped one arm
around her waist and bodily lifted her between
his legs. She was then kneeling in front of him on
the floor, and he was bending forward, slanting
his mouth down her neck, to the confining line of
her dress.

He buried his face and took a deep breath,
while one hand crept around her ribcage to stroke

at a slight, rounded breast. She held his head, bent over it, staring blindly at the sleek line of his back curved in front of her. Then he gently loosened his hold on her, pulled up, and kissed her one more time on the lips, lightly.

She was in a state of incomprehension. Staring at him with her dilated, immense eyes, she waited for some kind of explanation, unaware she was pleading silently. She saw him look deeply into her eyes, his own widening, and then he screwed them shut and swallowed. 'Don't look at me that way,' he whispered.

He didn't see how her face quivered, as if struck. 'Right,' she said then, and pulled away. A quick move from him, and he had her caught, his hands to her shoulders.

He opened his mouth to say something, hesitated as he saw her closed expression, and brought a hand up to cup at her cheek. 'I——' he started. 'I'd better be leaving. Supper tomorrow?'

'Sure,' she replied flatly. It caused a swift frown to plummet between his black brows. He let her go and, after she climbed to her feet, he rose. Without a word, they went into the hall, and she handed to him first his suit jacket, and then his overcoat, which he didn't bother to put on. He looked searchingly into her eyes, but she refused to look into his face, and walked over to the front door to unlock and open it.

He paused in the doorway, and then turned back. 'Shall I pick you up at six?'

'Fine.' Brief, terse.

His dark head was bent to her, and he was too close. He made a movement as if to kiss her good

night, and she stepped back from the touch,
which had him freezing quite still for a moment.
'Don't be this way,' he said in a low voice.

She smiled, mockingly. 'Why, I don't know
what you mean. I am what I am.'

He turned to the black night and walked away,
without replying. Her glittering smile faded as if
it had never been, and she wearily shut the door
on the cold.

Caprice went through the downstairs rooms,
switching off most of the lights except the one in
the hallway which was always left on, and then
she took her shoes and padded up to her room.
She locked her door, went to her bathroom to
cream off her make-up, and then slipped into
night clothes, turned down her sheet and covers,
and, with a flick of her wrist, put the room into
darkness. And for the rest of the night she
concentrated quite furiously on not thinking
about her evening spent with Pierce.

By the next morning, she knew she had made a
big mistake. She never should have agreed to
spend time with Pierce. She had been attracted to
him from the very beginning, and last night had
shown her just how far that attraction had gone.
Their encounter last night had been almost
virginal, and yet all her senses had leaped out of
control. Then she had to top it off by acting like a
disappointed nymphomaniac, and the memory of
that burned.

If she had thought she could have salvaged
her pride, she would have called him up and
pleaded sickness to get out of their date that

evening. But he would know better. He always knew better.

Her cheeks flamed hot, and she pressed her hands against them in mortification. Last night she had acted like such a fool, when he hadn't appeared to be deeply affected at all. This was wrong, all wrong, and especially so since she was the one who was in danger of getting badly hurt. Her eyes narrowed on the opposite wall of her bedroom as she brooded in bed. She would have to try to get out of tonight, somehow. She had no intention of being alone with Pierce again. It proved to be too devastating.

She lazed in bed until quite late, and only grudgingly rose to shower and dress. No skipping down the stairs today. She slunk down, blonde brow furrowed, and lower lip thrust out in thought, but she still hadn't come up with a solution when Liz informed her that she had a phone call.

It was Pierce. 'Hallo,' he said, sounding disembodied. She was fiercely glad he wasn't in front of her for, infuriatingly, her cheeks flamed again. She would have to get in control by that evening, no doubt about it.

'Hallo, yourself,' she said, cheerfully enough. 'What can I do for you?'

'Busy this afternoon?'

With a feeling of maliciousness that was quite disproportionate, she said gently, 'Alas, yes. What did you have in mind?'

'Nothing that won't keep for another time. I should have thought to ask you earlier. Well, I guess I'll see you this evening, then.'

'What—kind of restaurant did you have in mind, so that I can dress accordingly?' she asked quickly, the beginnings of an idea forming at the back of her mind.

'I thought we'd stay in town, if you don't mind. I have an early morning flight tomorrow at an ungodly hour.' He named a place she was well familiar with, and they rang off right after.

She had it, she definitely had it. She called Roxanne, who answered with a clearly audible yawn. Caprice grinned. 'Sleep late, too?'

'Yeah,' the other girl mumbled. 'What's up?'

'I need a favour.' She glanced up and down the hall, finding herself quite alone, which suited her just fine.

'Name it. Anything but money, and it's yours.'

'Poor thing,' she said commiseratingly. 'Hold tight. The first of the month is coming up quick.' A snort greeted that. 'Listen, have you got someone you could call up to take you out this evening?'

'What kind of favour is that?' Roxanne demanded. 'Yes, sure.'

'I'm eating out tonight, with Pierce Langston, and I can't cry off without him suspecting,' she began.

'Good God, why would you want to?' was the brunette's expostulation.

'Ah, it's a long story. Look, I'll explain some other time, OK? Now, what I want is for you two to show up at the restaurant around six-thirty this evening, and we can sort of team up for supper, all right?'

'Well, if that's what you really want——' Roxanne said doubtfully.

Caprice cut the other girl short. 'Believe me, I'm quite serious. Please, Rox?'

'You got it, kiddo.'

They hung up after a comfortable talk. The evening was taken care of, after all. Caprice told herself she was relieved.

She spent her afternoon leisurely, and dressed for the evening in a peach dress, which delicately brought out the sun-kissed quality of her deep tan. She let her fair fall loose to her shoulders, touched a light shade of cinnamon shadow to her eyes, with a matching shade of colour on her lips, and she was ready.

Pierce was quite prompt this time, and as the family was gathered in the den for drinks before supper, they were invited to stay. But when he looked to her enquiringly, one black brow raised, she shook her head, and so they soon left.

As he pulled out of the driveway, driving the Jaguar again, he said quietly, frowning at the road, 'You look lovely this evening. That dress suits you perfectly.'

She smiled as she stared out of her window at the passing streets, flattered by the compliment. 'Thank you. You know, you don't look so bad, yourself.' At that, he laughed, but the sound was short lived, quickly dying away.

Sunday usually meant rather less restaurant business, and so they were seated soon enough, without reservations. Caprice sat back and perused an already familiar menu while Pierce ordered a bottle of house wine.

When the waiter had left, he leaned forward, his own menu open and disregarded in front of him. 'I want to talk about last night,' he said softly.

That brought her eyes up with a jerk. They sparkled, brilliant, angry, and then she lowered her lids again and distantly ran her eyes over the meal selection. 'Oh, you do,' she said, absently. 'I don't, particularly.' She put her finger to one item, and frowned. 'Now, I can't remember if I've tried that and liked it, or tried it and didn't like it. Maybe it was this one.'

'Don't you want an explanation from me, or anything at all?' he pressed, voice going even lower. She could feel his hardening gaze boring into her like a physical drill.

'Hm? About what?' she murmured, turning the page and looking over the dessert section with every appearance of interest. She didn't see a thing.

'About why I left like I did.'

She glanced up quickly, blonde brows slightly raised. His jaw was slightly thrust out, the mouth hard, his eyes showing the beginnings of anger. 'No,' she said simply.

'I'd advise you to cut the act,' he said, almost gently. 'It just doesn't wash with me.'

'I'm not acting,' she said, deliberately innocent. There was an angry satisfaction in watching his face clench tight. He was angrier than she'd ever seen him before. With a chill down her spine, she suddenly wondered about their drive back to her house.

'Quit pretending to be so damned obtuse,' he whispered between his teeth, eyes glittering. 'What are you going to do, run away again when you could learn something?'

She smiled, inwardly so furious she could hardly sit still, and said with great charm, 'I will do anything I please.'

His eyes flicked behind her uninterestedly, and then sharpened. She watched as he positively spat out, 'Goddammit!' By that, she knew her relief had arrived.

Roxanne said from behind her, sounding quite surprised, 'Pierce—and Caprice. Hello, you two.' She let her eyes dwell admiringly on Pierce's grim profile. 'I didn't know you were seeing each other.'

Caprice looked up, eyes still snapping. 'A recent development,' she said flippantly. Her eyes flicked behind Roxanne, and her expression lightened to a genuine smile. 'How are you, Kurt? It's been a while since I've seen you.'

'Fine, just fine,' said the young man, greeting her with a flattering warmth. 'And how about yourself? You're looking terrific.'

She laughed with pleasure, glanced at Pierce and saw his blank, polite expression and knew he was still very angry. Roxanne blinked at the table, ingenuously. 'Have you two eaten yet?'

'Oh, no,' Caprice said, looking around herself. 'Would you both like to join us?'

Another glance risked at Pierce revealed absolutely nothing, but Kurt must have sensed something, for he started to say, 'I don't know——'

'We'd love to!' Roxanne gushed, and Caprice could have thrown her arms around the other girl and kissed her.

And so two more chairs were brought to the

table. Pierce still sat opposite, for which she was thankful. She couldn't tell if he suspected anything or not. There was certainly no fault to be found in his manners to the other couple. In fact, she found it a bit chilling to see how well he could cover up his true feelings. It left her wondering if perhaps he had acted the same with her, and if so, when.

She treated them all with warmth, never refusing to look Pierce straight in the eye, or to say something to him directly, and she could feel the brunette's puzzled, questioning gaze on her from time to time. Was she playing her own role that well then? Was this a habit she'd got into, over her lifetime? Had she played it for so long, she no longer knew if she was fooling herself or not?

None of the deep trouble these questions brought her showed in her lively, cheerful face.

After the meal, when they were waiting for their ordered coffee, Caprice began to feel the strain and stood, murmuring, 'Excuse me, please.' The men rose, also, as she picked up her bag and went in search of the ladies' room.

She heard, as she walked away from the table, Roxanne's voice, and the other girl rushed to catch up with her. After they were well away from the other two, Roxanne said quietly, 'What's going on between you two?'

Caprice pushed through the swinging door and went over to the opposite wall, where mirrors and a counter lined it from end to end. 'I don't know,' she admitted, and her voice was harsh. She slapped her handbag down, and opened it with shaking fingers. With determined calm, she drew out her brush and unnecessarily straightened her hair.

'The atmosphere was so thick when we walked up, I thought for sure we would slam into it. He looked angry.' Roxanne was watching her closely.

'We were having an argument,' she said, and bowed to put her face into her hands. Her shoulders shuddered once, and then she was back in control, shocked at her own loss of composure, her own reaction. 'I'm not going to see him after this.'

She went back to her grooming, touched lipstick at her lips carefully, and added blush to her pale cheeks. Roxanne stared at her for a few moments before turning her attention to her own appearance. 'I'm sure that's best,' she said. But she didn't sound sure. She sounded worried, and doubtful.

Before they went back to the table, Caprice looked hard at herself, and saw the beginning of tiny lines of stress on either side of her mouth, along with the faint smudges appearing under her large eyes. She stood quite still. Then she wiped all expression away, and put on a placid smile. The change was incredible, and Roxanne blinked before nodding to her encouragingly as they went out the door.

The coffee was served, the two men at their ease with each other, and the rest of the time fairly flew by, until the bill was paid and the tip laid down on the table, and they were all leaving. Pierce had his hand to her back as she gave the others one last wave, and then they made their way to the Jaguar in silence.

The evening was more balmy than it had been last night, the breeze refreshing instead of chilling, swaying through trees and telephone and electric lines in an ever-present, restless sound. Pierce unlocked the passenger door and attentively saw her seated within before moving to the driver's side.

He hadn't said a thing, hadn't shown any difference in his behaviour after leaving the other two, and yet she tensed, from neck muscles down to her thighs, as he started the car up with a low purr, and backed smoothly out of the car park. After a few moments, he said conversationally, 'You invited them to stay for supper on purpose, didn't you?'

She might prevaricate with someone else, but she knew better with him. 'Yes,' she said, shortly.

The Jaguar picked up speed. She doubted if he even realised. 'Who are you afraid of, yourself or me?'

That stung. Why did it sting? She replied sharply, 'I'm not afraid of anyone!' Without the softening effects of low music being played, the words resounded terribly in the silence of the car. She lowered her voice. 'I don't know what you mean.'

'Sure you do. You're not stupid, you just like to act it,' he said quite savagely. She stared out of her window, wishing they were already home. It was a short drive, but it seemed to be taking forever. They were both tense and quiet for the next few minutes. Then he said, 'I shouldn't have said that. I'm sorry.'

Oh yes, she had it figured out now. That dull

ache in her chest was her heart. But the personality wasn't in the heart, was it? It was in the brain, running electric currents which made her feel so miserable at times, and so good at others. 'You call them as you see them,' she said flippantly.

'*Stop* it,' he said, low-voiced. She looked over to him and saw how his hands were clenched, bone-white, on the wheel. They were nearing the house. She bowed her head, and sighed wearily. Funny. She knew it would be goodbye, but he didn't. It was better that way. He pulled into the driveway, and switched off the engine. Then he sighed and rubbed at the bridge of his nose as if he were tired, and he leaned his head back against the seat like he had yesterday. Strange, how different things were from yesterday. 'I have to go back, tomorrow.'

'I never thought any differently,' she said, quite surprised. She turned her blonde head in his general direction. 'Thanks for this evening. I hope you enjoyed their company.'

'No, I didn't.' He was quite flat about it. No polite nonsense from him.

'Well,' was her dry response. Her hand went fumbling for the car door. 'On that note, I think I shall say——'

From that instant on, everything changed. His dark head turned, swiftly, and she saw something burning at the back of his eyes. He said, very low, 'Get over here.' His hand snaked out, grabbed hold of her upper arm, and dragged her to him.

He held her head, fingers pressing their imprint against her skull as he passionately took

her mouth. She moaned involuntarily as his
tongue drove deep, without preliminaries.
Deeper, and yet deeper, driving into her with
frustration, with something impelling him on,
with his hands shifting her weight uncomfortably
over the gearstick so that she was sitting in his
lap, off-balance, and clutching at him. Her head
now lay nestled against his shoulder and her
weight was carrying her back. She was staring
blindly up at the car's ceiling as his mouth left
hers, and he emitted an audible, small groan as if
it were torn from him, slanting his mouth
hungrily along her throat as his hand dragged
away the shoulder of her wrap and dress. She was
barely aware of her hand sinking deep into his
hair as he found her breast and suckled excitedly.
All his muscles were rigid, and throbbing hard.
His whole body radiated his tension, bewilder-
ingly.

This wasn't the man who was so cool and
controlled last night. This was the man of last
weekend, exuding unleashed, powerful passion.
This was the man who scared and excited her half
to death. Her head came up and leaned into the
straining, bent muscles in his neck as she
whimpered, without even realising it, from the
force of her confused emotions and desires.

He stopped gradually, leaning his face into her
bare chest, breathing harsh and deep. His
muscles relaxed, and he raised his head, expression blank, intent. He was in full control once
again, and she didn't know if she was disappointed
or not. He cradled her briefly against him, and
only then seemed to realise how awkward her

position was, and he helped her back to her side of the car, waiting until she had straightened her appearance.

Then he walked her to the door, saying quietly, 'This week is going to be hectic for me, so I can't say exactly when, but I'll give you a call.'

'Sure,' she said, and she hadn't meant it to come out so sarcastically.

'I will,' he insisted, staring into her eyes hard. He looked troubled and seemed about to say something when he caught himself up and shook his head, slight and quick, as if impatient with himself. 'I promise.'

As there was nothing left to say, he pressed her already swollen lips with another hard kiss, and sprinted back to the car. Her fingers went to the cool metal of the front doorknob, and she dragged herself inside, knowing full well she had no intention of taking the call he'd been so adamant about promising.

CHAPTER NINE

SHE basked in the mellow golden sun's rays, clad in her briefest swimsuit and stretched comfortably on a lounge chair, with sunglasses perched on her nose and a frown between her brows. It was a valiant effort to concentrate on her book. Several more, brand new, were stacked on the grass beside her.

Thursday already, and he hadn't called. Perhaps he never would. Well. She had resolved not to take the call, anyway, if he did. She had also changed her mind half a dozen times in the last four days. He wouldn't come up this weekend, without encouragement. That was best.

The problem was, if she had no intention of taking his call, why did she refuse all social invitations just to stay home? And there was the party Roxanne's mother was giving on Saturday. She had already been asked by several of her acquaintances, and she'd turned them all down. She was a fool for expecting him to fly down to Virginia. It had to be a clean break, with Pierce. With some men, it didn't have to be that way, but with him, it was different, as it had always been different.

Her heart was tangled into knots over him, and she didn't know how to get herself out of it.

Lazy movement from her left made her look up. Ricky strolled her way, in shorts and tennis shoes and nothing else, and he flopped beside her in the grass. 'Whew! My muscles are melting.' He turned his head and squinted up at her. 'You don't need those sunglasses. Hand them over.'

'Take a hike,' she muttered serenely, turning a page in her book. He grinned, and then peered closely at her paperback.

Suddenly he was all concern, as he came up on both knees and pressed the fingers of one hand against her forehead. 'Do you feel sick? Good God, I think you have a fever.'

She shrugged his hand away laughingly. 'What's got into you? Cut it out!'

'I think I should be the one to ask that!' he retorted. He shifted to the other side of her chair, and picked up her stack of books. 'You're seriously reading this stuff, for fun? Kierkegaard, Pierre Teilhard de Chardin's *Hymn of the Universe*, ye gods! Karl Marx, Franz Kafka—what has got into you?'

'Just because I've graduated from college doesn't mean my education has to stop,' she said waspishly, and gave up trying to concentrate on her book. She closed it with a snap, bringing Ricky's attention to it. It was Kafka's *The Metamorphosis*, and he picked it up from her lap to leaf through it.

'You're not just skimming, are you?'

'Of course not! I'm close to finished with that one.'

'Have you read any of the others?'

'Not yet. That's the first I've read. I picked it because it's the shortest,' she confessed, with a grin.

He laughed, and handed it back to her. 'Well, is it any good? What happens?'

She shrugged. 'Some guy turns into a bug.' She listened to his snort, and then she became serious, picking up the book and fiddling with it absently. 'It actually isn't as stupid as it sounds. It's bizarre, certainly, but very haunting.' Her voice turned dreamy. 'Think about it for a moment. Changing into something new, something alien, something different. Your life is changed forever. Your family and friends shun you. You pine away from lack of proper nourishment, and then you—die.'

'Mmm. But is that a realistic portrayal? I mean, not of course in the physical sense, but mentally people change all the time.'

She shook her head slowly. 'No. People grow, but to *change*, Ricky, is something entirely different. It's like taking a leap sideways, leaving accepted patterns of behaviour, making people realise that their concept of you is no longer accurate. Think of what it would do to your life. It's an utterly terrifying thought.'

Silence, settling over them and the scene like a sprinkling of windblown pollen. A bird winged by with the enthusiasm of a mad bomber. An immense grasshopper bounced his way across the immaculate lawn. 'But Caprice,' said Ricky quietly, 'unless someone changes from Doctor Jekyll to Mr Hyde, it's perfectly acceptable. Nobody changes so completely that there's nothing left in them that is recognisable. It might even be for the good.'

*   *   *

By Friday, she had decided recklessly to take
his call, and damn the consequences. She
longed to see him. She couldn't get last Sunday
evening out of her mind. The memory of his
mouth on her breast nipple stirred her to sexual
excitement; his passion brought her a wave of
heat. She had never been so tugged by physical
sensation and emotional desire. They were one
and the same, intertwined so that she couldn't
distinguish between them. It boiled down to
pure, unadulterated lust, and she winced away
from the thought, disturbed. She wanted his
mouth, his hands, and his affection. She was
beginning to want it past all thought of future
happiness.

But then he didn't call, and by late evening he
still hadn't called, leaving her to stew in a welter
of feverish emotions. Just as suddenly as she'd
decided to take his call, she swung back to
refusing it in a fit of pique. Nobody could be that
busy. He could have called even for a minute or
two any evening during the week. She didn't
know what he was thinking or planning, but
she'd had enough. This prolonged, intensified
anticipation was extremely wearying and certainly
not pleasurable.

Saturday morning, she was dressed in casual
shorts and tank top, sipping listlessly at her coffee
while trying to decide what to do with herself
before the party, when Liz walked into the dining
room. 'You've got a phone call,' said the
housekeeper.

Her cup went to her saucer with a cacophonic
clatter. 'Who——' she began, but decided she

didn't want to know. Her jaw tightened. 'I'm not home.'

'Are you sure?' asked Liz, clearly puzzled. 'He said you were expecting it.'

She pushed her coffee away, and jerkily stood. 'I'm positive. I'm not talking to anyone today.' Ignoring the other woman's speculative stare, she stalked out of the room. She stopped dead, turned back to take the call and, cursing, turned around again.

'Before, I had my doubts, but this definitely clinches it,' said Ricky from the stairs. He descended the rest of the way. 'You're going crazy so fast, you can't keep up with yourself. Like spinning in circles?'

'Oh, shut up!' she said savagely.

He pretended to be frightened and drew back from her with a shudder. 'Well! I was going to ask you if you wanted to play tennis, but you might bite my head off, instead of answering in a civilised manner.'

'Always knew you were a coward,' she grumbled, with a partial return of good humour.

'Like to play tennis?'

'Not really. Oh, I guess so. There's nothing else to do!'

'A split personality, forming before my very eyes,' he marvelled. Then, sagely, 'They're quite rare, you know. I'll write a book about you, and astonish the psychology world.'

'Get the racquets, smart ass,' she said, grinning reluctantly. 'I'm going to plaster you all over the court.'

'Bloodthirsty to boot!' he exclaimed, delightedly.

Ricky made her laugh with his clowning, and she was nearly light-hearted, tossing her tennis ball up in their air while sending an evil glare to her unaffected opponent. Then she glanced casually over towards the house, as she was facing in that direction, and froze into rigidity.

Pierce was dressed in faded jeans, tennis shoes, and a light blue, sleeveless T-shirt. She'd never seen him so carelessly dressed. His hair was windblown and in glossy disarray, and he was staring intently at her as he strolled her way.

She abandoned her serving pose and stood with bent, averted head and grim expression as she bounced the ball hard upon the court, catching it with a swipe of her hand. 'What's up?' called Ricky, obviously not seeing Pierce yet.

'We'll play later,' she said shortly, and watched as his head turned towards Pierce, and then back to herself.

'Yeah, sure,' he replied, shifting from foot to foot in uncharacteristic uncertainty. He sent her one more questioning look, and then silently headed back for the house.

Pierce approached in an indolent manner, hands in pockets, and then looked about him appreciatively, eyes squinted against the glare of the sun. She avoided meeting his eyes. 'You didn't have to quit playing,' he said. 'I'd have waited.' She didn't say anything, feeling his quick, sharp regard. 'Of course, you didn't have to lie, either.'

'Would you have accepted that I didn't want to talk to you?' she retorted, striding over to the edge of the court to throw down her racquet and the tennis ball. When she glanced back over her shoulder, she was amazed to find that he didn't appear angry.

'I don't know. You didn't give me the chance,' he pointed out, his gaze steady. At her raised, sardonic brow he relented. 'All right. Probably not.'

An awkward silence fell over them both. She longed to walk away, but didn't know where she would go, for he would certainly follow. She longed to turn around and greet him with the pleasure she wouldn't let herself feel. What she did was to say, 'I didn't know you'd be coming this weekend.'

'If you'd taken my call, you would have,' he retorted, the snappiness revealing at last his frustration. He walked over to her side and stared down into her rebellious, miserable expression with a frown between his sleek brows. He sighed, and bent his head to rub at the back of his neck. 'Caprice, what am I going to do with you?'

'You could always go back to New York,' she said tightly. 'Start dating women there, if you've stopped. Less commuting that way.' It should have come out flippant, but instead it sounded choked.

He stepped nearer, and everything in her body tugged her towards him, but she wouldn't move. Then gentle fingers stroked her cheek and jawline, moving under her hair to tuck it back. 'I don't go for casual dating,' he said softly. 'It bores me. It's shallow, and needlessly expensive, and emotionally unrewarding.' She couldn't help herself, and rubbed her cheek against his hand, much like she had last Saturday, when things between them had changed to become confusing, upsetting. *Sexual*.

His hand was opening to cup her cheek when she jerked her head away, flushing darkly. His hand dropped to his side. 'Will you see me tonight?' he asked, quite calmly.

She gave a little, incredulous laugh at his persistence, unamused and dying instantly. 'I'm going to a party,' she half whispered, and scuffed her shoe in the grass. 'Everybody's going.'

'Who's taking you?'

She could have lied again. She could have dredged up a last-minute escort; she was popular enough for that. She could have prevaricated in a thousand ways, but her mind was frozen and her lips were already shaping, in a thread of whisper, 'No one.'

His hand came under her chin, fingers caressing her skin, and then he lifted her face to stare into her huge eyes. 'When shall I pick you up?' he asked firmly.

For a long moment she searched his eyes, seeing nothing but determination and steadiness. 'Seven,' she said.

'See you tonight,' he told her, and before she could move or ascertain what he was going to do, he bent and swiftly kissed her on the mouth. She watched him walk away, her mind a whirling blank.

After some time, realising she was alone, she bent to pick up the racquet and popped the ball back into its container, and then headed slowly back for the house. Inside, she met her mother, who detained her with a hand on her arm.

'Dear, wasn't that Pierce who just drove away?' Irene asked.

'Yes.' She attempted a tentative tug to get herself free, but her mother was having none of it.

'What an extraordinary amount of attention he's been paying you! And how flattering, to have him fly down from New York on the weekends! Tell me, are you seeing him again?'

'He's taking me to the party tonight, but it doesn't mean anything,' she told Irene, and finally managed to pull herself free. 'Please, don't make more out of it than there really is. I may never go out with him again!'

'Nonsense, he's such a handsome, polite young man!' her mother marvelled. Caprice felt something surge up inside of her, and pinched her lips against it. 'And everybody knows how successful the Langston family business is! Why, your Pierce is a very good catch——'

'Is that all you can think of, Mother?' she burst out, shocking Irene to silence. 'My God, he could be a child molester or a wife beater, for all you know of him! You've talked with him once, and you've met him twice, and all you can see are his money and his looks! Doesn't anything else matter to you?'

Her voice rang through the hall. For a moment, mother and daughter stared into each other's eyes, widened, both stricken, and then Caprice whirled and ran up to her room, to lock herself into privacy.

*   *   *

Again, she was dressed and downstairs on time, having no use for senseless dallying. Her parents were just preparing to leave, clad in formal evening attire and looking splendid. Ricky had left some time before, as he was escorting a young girl his own age. Caprice knew her, and was secretly amused at his choice, for she was every bit his match in wits and was quick with sharp retorts. His usual style was the brainless, ornamental type. She rather thought she should seriously fear for his heart.

She wished her parents a stilted farewell, for Irene was steadfastly not looking at her and Richard was clearly aware of it and quite puzzled. As they left, she shut the door behind them, and checked the time on the clock in the hall. She had forsaken her wristwatch for the evening, as she was dressed in sleek midnight blue, which was gathered off one slender shoulder and fell in straight, severe lines to mid-calf. The only ornamentation she wore was a winking silver anklet atop her thin-strapped, blue sandals which raised her a good three inches higher.

She checked her make-up carefully one last time, and the doorbell rang. Furious at her leaping heart, she took two calming breaths, and then went serenely to answer the summons.

But she was in for another leap in heart, for Pierce's appearance seemed to destroy her composure. Black, straight-cut legs, hands tucked carelessly into his pockets with the suit jacket pulled back, revealing a tight waistcoat and bow tie stark against the white of his shirt, hair immaculate, face unsmiling, seeming remote, all this she took in at a glance.

His eyes swept over her, black sparkling bright, and widened. 'I see you're ready.'

She swallowed past something in her throat. 'Let me get my wrap and bag,' she said, and hurried back to the den to retrieve them. He stepped into the hall while he waited, and then stood back from the door as she joined him. The familiar gesture of his hand to her back escorted her to the car, and they started to the Cauleighs'.

'You look absolutely lovely,' he said quietly, after she had given him directions.

She was thankful for the darkness in the car, for she blushed like a gauche sixteen-year-old. 'So do you,' she said, surprising herself and him.

He laughed, the first she'd heard since that rather grim morning encounter, and her spirits lightened unaccountably. They were soon pulling up to the Cauleighs' house, which was ablaze with outside lights and new arrivals. When he smoothly parked beside the road, though there were several parking places still available alongside the long driveway, she questioned him about it, to which he drily replied, 'My dear, I have no intention of being blocked in till the wee hours of the morning.' He switched off the engine, and turned in his seat to look at her from under level brows. 'I want to talk to you, later this evening. I'd like to leave the party early.' When she didn't answer right away, he lifted an eyebrow. 'Well?'

'Well, what?' She turned to open her car door, and was stopped by his hand on her wrist. 'We'll just have to see.'

'That's no answer.' He was implacable, not about to let her slide on this one.

She raised cool brows to him, and replied lightly, 'But then I never said I would give you an answer. What I said was, we shall see.'

His mouth tightened ominously, but when she tugged her arm, he let her go, and so they went to the party.

She knew almost everyone invited, but Pierce, having lost touch with people in Virginia now for several years, had to be introduced to quite a few. When Caprice caught sight of Roxanne, she excused herself from Pierce's side and made her way over to the brunette, who was looking particularly vibrant in a cocktail dress of deep cherry red.

Roxanne flashed her a bright smile, pulled away from Kurt, and said in a low undertone, 'Thought you weren't going to be seeing him any more.'

Caprice felt the flush that washed over her features as a burning hot sensation. 'It's—hard to explain,' she murmured. 'He's—It just happened this morning.'

'I see.' The brunette's eyes rested on her, bright, piercing, not unkindly. 'Don't hurt yourself, babe.'

Caprice's jaw clenched. 'I'm trying to avoid that at all costs,' was her grim muttered reply. She said a quick goodbye, with the promise of getting together later to talk, and then she began to make her way back to Pierce, who was leaning against the back of a chair while talking with an older gentleman, whose young wife clung to his arm and gazed with wide-eyed fascination at the younger man. According to the rumours, she had married the older man for his money, and from the way her eyes ate Pierce up, every lean inch of him, the rumours were true.

Half-way across the large, crowded room, Caprice bumped into a man who backed up unexpectedly. Quick hands shot out to steady her toppling balance, and she laughed as she said, 'A good thing I didn't have a drink in one hand! Emory! How are you?'

Emory's blond brows shot up, and delight lightened his whole countenance. 'Caprice! We were looking for you.' He gave her an affectionate hug. 'I have some good news.'

She turned her head, and looked into Petra's friendly eyes. Her grin turned naughty, as her eyes shot swiftly down to the other woman's left hand. A large engagement ring winked brightly, and as Petra saw the direction of her gaze, she brought up her hand and displayed the diamond for Caprice's approval. 'Well, it's about time!' she exclaimed, laughing again. 'You know, he almost gave up on you!'

'Yes,' replied the other girl, with mortification. 'He told me all about it. It was a stupid misunderstanding from the very start. And I want to apologise to you. I was thinking some very nasty things about you that weekend. It was all jealousy, and very unfair. I'm so sorry.'

'Nonsense,' said Caprice lightly, reaching up to Emory's tie to twitch at it mischievously. 'You thought precisely what I wanted you to think, my dear. I deserved every wicked thing you thought.'

As she walked away, she was treated to the sight of Petra actually whooping, while Emory's face bore a most ludicrous expression of surprise.

Somehow, after being from Pierce's side for more than a half hour, it became easier and easier to find some excuse to stay away. She flitted from person to person, flirting with every man in the room, regardless of age, and was actually beginning to enjoy herself. A small cluster formed around her in one corner, where she stayed for some time, chattering away. Occasionally she would scan the room to see where Pierce was, and he always seemed to be deep in conversation with someone, and quite often that someone was feminine, which, she told herself, was a very good thing. That way she didn't have to feel guilty for deserting him, as she would if he'd been left stranded and at a loss.

But he was handling himself quite well, almost too well. She hadn't expected anything else, necessarily, for he was too mature and poised to do otherwise. But did he have to look so content without her company? Didn't he feel the slightest bit jealous?

Her party smile slipped for a moment, and badly. She wasn't enjoying herself at all, at all, and she wanted to go home. Then the young man who was talking to her said something with a questioning note at the end of it, and she dragged herself back and racked her memory for what it was that he had said.

The Cauleighs' house was bursting with people. The Langstons were present, including Jeffrey, who avoided her gaze and kept discreetly away from wherever she happened to be. She noted it with some wryness, as he'd always been annoyingly attentive before, and she couldn't help but wonder if this new behaviour was because he knew she was seeing Pierce, or because of shame for how he had acted two weeks ago. Her luck with the Langston brothers did not seem to be running well at the moment.

Then she turned her head, by pure chance, and caught her mother's troubled gaze resting on her. They stared at each other from across the room, wordlessly. 'Excuse me,' said Caprice to her attendant, cutting through what he'd been saying in mid-sentence. Even as he blinked and shut his mouth, in somewhat belated response, she was making her way over to Irene and Richard.

Irene turned to her husband and said something in his ear, to which he nodded, and he left her side without seeing Caprice. Mother and daughter then stood side by side for a few moments, without speaking.

'Nice party,' said Caprice falsely, and her mother murmured a too bright reply, party smile fastened firmly in place. Caprice looked past the mask and saw the faint glitter in Irene's eyes. 'Mom,' she said then, laying her hand gently on the older woman's sleeve. 'I'm sorry.'

'Why, for heaven's sake?' said Irene, with an odd little laugh that wasn't a laugh at all. 'For being right?'

'No,' she said very quietly, feeling something like grief well up inside her for the other, foolish woman's pain. 'For telling you like I did. I was cruel, I hurt you, and I'm sorry.'

Beyond both women's sight, Richard slowed and stopped, waiting for the two to finish in some semblance of privacy while he held two drinks. After a moment, Irene met her daughter's remorseful gaze with a real smile. 'I still think Pierce is a fine man,' she said simply.

Caprice laughed. 'So do I, Mom. So do I.' She bent forward, pressed a quick kiss to her mother's cheek, and then whisked away again, in search of different, amusing company.

She didn't know what she thought. She supposed, later, that she knew it couldn't last for too long, that she was silently goading Pierce, that she was being rude. She did know that, as the evening progressed, she felt worse. She did know that every time she saw Pierce appearing to be interested in any woman of decent figure and age, she felt something dart like needles into her. But she couldn't think why it hurt, or why she was acting the way she was, or why he put up with it. It was as unfathomable as a murky lake at full night, nothing to be seen or understood past the shallow ripples.

There came a time when, as she was chattering away with a presentable young man who showed unmistakable signs of infatuation, Pierce strolled up to stand beside her. 'Excuse me,' he said, without interest, to the young man. Without even waiting for the other to question him or withdraw politely, he turned to her and said, 'I've had enough. I'm leaving now. If you would like to come with me, you may, and if not, then I'm sure your parents will be more than happy to see you home.'

She was unprepared for the ultimatum, or the cavalier manner in which he presented it. That she might have deserved it didn't come into the matter; she felt a sudden wave of rage wash over her, and with her eyes sparkling like hard stones, she said between her teeth, 'Don't you dare issue orders to me, do you hear?'

Pierce turned to the presentable young man and said pleasantly, 'Now, did you hear me issuing any orders? I thought not.' He turned back to her. 'I merely informed you of your choices.'

The presentable young man looked extremely uncomfortable, gabbled something which was supposed to be polite or witty, and backed quickly away. Neither noticed.

Caprice had never been treated that way in her entire life. Men always came and went at her bidding, not the other way around. She couldn't believe her ears. 'Do you mean, you would actually walk out on someone you escorted to a party?'

Incredibly, he smiled. 'Yes,' he said. 'So, which is it to be? Either you come with me now and we have that talk I've been waiting for all evening, or I walk out of here, and that's it. I won't be commuting any more to Virginia. It's quite a clear-cut choice, I should think.'

Shock hit her anew. Somehow, she hadn't been expecting it to be this way. Somehow she'd been expecting to be the one to call things off, whenever it suited her. Her huge, violet eyes quickly searched his, and she found nothing in them but a smiling steeliness. 'You're just angry,' she said, attempting to shrug it off. But her voice sounded uncertain.

He raised his brows. 'Wherever did you get that idea?' he asked, sounding genuinely surprised. 'Perhaps you think I have cause to be?' That sent colour to her cheeks. 'But no, I'm not. I think I'm beginning to understand you a little better—not a whole lot, God knows! Your mind works in truly tortuous ways. But I certainly don't feel angry with you tonight, merely a bit bored. I can watch you talk with someone else for only so long, I'm afraid. Now, for the final time, which is it to be? I've had your wrap brought down.'

He didn't even sound concerned, and that hurt and angered her the most. Without thinking, she spat out, 'I'm not ready to leave, yet!'

Something in his pleasant, blank face flickered then. 'I see. Good night, then, sweetheart.' He pressed a quick, light kiss to her cheek and turned to walk away.

She watched him leave, feeling cold and stiff. Something began a hard pounding in her heart. He went into the hall and was out of sight. She looked around, at the people packed in the room, milling about, talking to one another about things that were certainly interesting, but by no means crucial to her happiness. She was left with nothing crucial to her happiness, just a lot of pleasantries which meant nothing at all to her.

She was racing for the door in the next instant, bumping through people, whisking around the woman who held her wrap and yanking it out of

her hands without bothering to excuse herself or
to even say thank you. Then she was at the front
door, wondering if she was too late, throwing it
open wide.

CHAPTER TEN

'WAIT!' she cried, straining her eyes to peer through the darkness. She hurried down the front steps towards the driveway. A patch of shadow that was Pierce's black suit stopped suddenly still, and whirled round. She had reached the driveway by then, and her steps faltered to a stop as her eyes adjusted to the night and she took in his rigid stance. He wasn't as indifferent as he seemed. 'I'll come,' she said, voice sounding thin in the open air. 'But I don't make any promises.' Despite her words, she hovered uncertainly, unsure if his offer was still open.

She hadn't realised how much it meant to her, until she saw his hand come up wordlessly, palm outstretched in invitation. She sighed harshly in sagging reaction, her wrap crushed against her chest in her arms. The knowledge bolted through her, then, that if he would but call her name, she would follow him anywhere he asked. Her shaking legs found the impetus to carry her forward to him, to take his hand, but instead of closing his fingers around hers, he drew her evening wrap out of her arms, draped it carefully about her slight figure, and then put his arm around her shoulders. In that way they walked to the car.

Caprice's mind and heart were reeling. She didn't know how, or when, but she had managed

to fall deeply in love with him. Her lips shook.
Such a fine, cool-headed determination she'd
had, and, despite all her efforts, she would be the
one to get hurt.

She should have known from the beginning.
She should have seen. She knew that he was
different from the very start; she knew that what
she'd felt for him had been different. But she'd
never fallen in love before, and didn't know how
to recognise the signs of it in herself. She turned
her head as he courteously gave a hand to help
her into the Jaguar, averting her face. How could
anyone not love him? His gentleness, his quiet
poise, his understanding. It all made him
endearing to her. But what shook her to the core
was something in him, barely glimpsed or
understood, that lay beneath his other qualities
like a brooding, slumbering beast. It was a wealth
of passion and compassion, a stronghold of deep,
overpowering feeling, and it frightened her even
as it drew her close to its warmth.

He got into the car silently, started the engine,
and pulled on to the street. She was off-balance
and shaking. He was frowning and withdrawn,
his jawline hard as though he worked hard to
contain something.

When he missed the turn that took them to her
house, she blinked a few times, and flicked a
wary, sidelong glance to him. He seemed like a
stranger. 'Where are we going?' she asked
cautiously. 'Why aren't you taking me home?'

'I know from experience that Jeffrey and my
parents will be gone till quite late,' he said then,
almost absently. 'And the servants have the

evening off. I want you in privacy, so that I know we won't be disturbed, and that you can't run away, as seems to be your habit whenever I try to have a heart to heart talk with you.'

She put a hand to her forehead, letting her hair fall forward to hide her face. She wasn't in control. Everything about her was stupidly shaking. The slightest pressure from him, and she would crack up. 'Thanks for asking,' she said, bitterly.

'You made your choice.'

She'd never been to the Langston home. It seemed huge, easily twice the size of her own home, the yellow security lights illuminating great pools of deep red brick and creeping, mature ivy. Pierce parked the car, and turned in his seat to stare at her thoughtfully. She kept her eyes steadfastly trained on the dashboard ahead of her, expression tight. He lifted his hand and touched at her hair with the backs of his fingers. Then he climbed out of the car and, as there was nothing else for her to do, she followed.

Inside, he led her to a rather larger version of their den and, as she walked jerkily around the room, he mixed them drinks. She took her wrap and threw it carelessly to a chair, letting it slide between her fingers. The deep, brilliant blue of her dress and her silver blonde hair made her stand out from the muted browns in the background like a slim, cool flame. When he handed her a gin and tonic, she took the round, cold glass, carefully avoiding his fingers, and a wry twist of his well-shaped lips told her he knew it.

The silence stretched tight, magnified by the hulking weight of huge emptiness that expanded around them. The house was probably from the 1700s, she guessed by the architecture, and no doubt it creaked at night. She turned away from Pierce's tall figure and ran her eyes up to the ceiling. It was a lovely home.

'I love you,' he said quietly, and she spilled her drink.

'Oh God, I'm sorry,' she exclaimed breathlessly, her heart knocking ninety miles an hour in her chest. She set down her half-full glass with a sharp chink, and hurried to the bar in search of towels. It incidentally took her well away from Pierce, for which she was grateful.

'Leave it,' he said sharply, making an impatient gesture. 'The carpet doesn't matter.'

She found a towel, and turned to stare at the floor at his feet. 'But it should be cleaned before it soaks in too much——'

'I said leave it!' His voice rose harshly, and she dropped the towel in immediate reaction. 'Damn it, woman, I just said I love you! Does that do anything at all to you?'

Her hands flew to her face as she was stung into crying, 'What do you want me to say? That I love you, too, and let's go live happily ever after?'

He made a sharp, ungraceful movement towards her that she felt through her entire body, making her jump where she stood. 'Would that be so bad?' he replied, sounding ragged, quite unlike himself. 'What do you feel for me, Caprice? You act so differently from one moment to the next, I can't tell!'

She pulled her hands from her face to stare at them, the slender fingers, the oval palms. 'I— want to go home now,' she whispered, her eyes filling.

'What will it take to break through to you?' he shouted, and she visibly cringed. 'You're always running away, putting on an act, doing anything you possibly can to avoid something like this between us! Why? If you don't love me, for God's sake, just say so and it's the end of the discussion!'

'Don't,' she choked out. 'Oh, don't.'

He made a strange sort of sound that was more wrenched out of him than anything else, and he strode over to take her into his arms. With one hand, he cradled her bright head to his chest. 'And why do you tear me apart inside?' he whispered into her hair. 'All this week I thought of you. I tried to put you out of my mind so that I could get through work, but you were there when I least expected it. I heard your laugh, saw your smile, and all I wanted was to hold you.'

She found that she was clinging to him, knees shaking, weeping into his shirt as she tried to say coherently, 'But I never wanted to hurt you. I never wanted to hurt anyone.'

His hand fondled the back of her head, warm fingers, gentle touch. 'There's no reason to hurt anyone, or to be hurt, sweetheart. Just tell me how you feel. Let me into that heart and mind of yours so that I can understand you a little better! Can't you see that this is vitally important? I know you must care for me to some extent, I can sense that much.'

'You're moving too fast,' she whispered, shaking her head. 'You're pushing too hard!'

He went very still. Then his voice sounded in her ear, harsh, almost savage with the force of feeling behind it. 'I should have forced the issue last Saturday. I should have pushed then, but thought I should try to hold back for your sake.' He drew back, and forced her to meet his eyes. She saw grim hardness in his. 'At least I know one way to get to you.'

The tension in his body snapped. He came to a decision, she could feel it. In one swift movement, he bent and picked her up. Sheer shock held her immobile as he carried her into the hall and to the stairs.

'Pierce,' she strangled out, but he was unrelenting and his grip too tight for her to wriggle out of. 'My God!'

The next several seconds were a blurred rush, as she arched her body in frightened, stunned protest and he raced up the stairs with no apparent lessening of his stride when burdened with her weight. They passed into a room, he kicked the door shut behind him, and then he strode forward and threw her on to a bed.

Her body gave a bounce, but before she could thrust herself off the mattress, he fell on her. She held herself rigid and straight in blind fear, and then he took her head between his large hands and began to kiss her. He stroked her body in long, jerky strokes, cupping her breast through the material of her dress. His mouth was everywhere, black head moving urgently as he put his mouth on her neck, her forehead, her trembling jaw, chin, lips, anything he could reach.

Gradually realisation dawned, and she felt herself relax. He hadn't even tried to force his way past her lips. This was a man who knew very well how she was stirred physically by him. This was a man pleading with her, with everything in his body and soul. This was a man who was telling her he wanted her past pride and reservation, and he was letting her know it in any way he could.

She felt heat wash over her, and she groaned. Along with it came a severe bout of trembling. 'Oh, Pierce,' she whispered, and cupped his head with both hands.

He rose from pressing his lips to her collar bone and bare shoulder, and he came down to her mouth with a single-minded hungriness. Once she weakly opened her mouth to his, he plunged in deep. She made a whimpering sound, and thrust her fingers into his silken hair. He drew back, stared down at her with dark eyes that glittered hotly through the dusky shadow, and he whispered, 'Let me undress you.'

She drew in an unsteady breath, looking up at him. His hair fell on his brow, and she wasn't even aware when she reached up to smooth it back. 'I'm scared.'

The alien, bone-clenched expression on his face faded somewhat, and he took her hands to bring them gently to his chest, half lying on her heavily, half off, propped on one elbow. 'Don't think. Don't doubt. I love you. You want this. Put your hands on me. Help me take my clothes off.'

He was determined to pull her into full
participation. He was making her a partner,
forcing her to succumb to the rising, driving
response they both knew was inside her. When he
was completely naked, he made her touch every
part of his hot, tight body, and she was shaking
so that she could barely move her heavy limbs by
that time. She was in such a feverish welter of
desire that she twisted her body to him and
whispered, achingly, 'Why aren't you taking my
clothes off and touching me, too?'

He was tight, so tight, so hard and big and
masculine, with a light sheen of salty sweat on his
skin. Then the rigidity broke, and he began to
tremble, too. He gently pushed her back against
the pillows and looked deeply into her immense
eyes, his own dilated. His cheeks held a dark
flush. 'I love you, I want to make love with you, I
want to touch you all over and bury myself so
deep in you, I'll never find my way out again,' he
said, quick and hot and low. 'But most of all,
Caprice—most of all, I want and need to hear you
say that you love me, and know that you have the
courage to admit it. Otherwise,' he shook
everywhere, that strong, poised, contained man;
'otherwise this means nothing. I need it.' His
head lowered, until he was whispering the words,
lips touching lips. 'Tell me. Say it.'

He had made himself totally accessible and
vulnerable. He had bared himself to her, and
showed his own desire without shame. He had
taken the plunge alone, through the strength of
his emotion, to make her see that though love was
an unseen, unplundered depth, frightening and

life-changing, it could also be a wealth of comfort
and sensation and total sharing. Something in her
loosened. She was made to believe in the force of
his conviction. She said the words and then she
couldn't say them enough, as he gently slipped
her dress from her body and touched her then
with hands and mouth, for the love inside her
welled up, stronger and deeper with every
heartfelt caress from him. She stroked him then,
in excited, wondering acknowledgment.

They gave in to physical sensation and body
movement and a mutual, rhythmic desire, his
hard body over hers, his low, muttered voice
saying in her ear, 'Love me. Don't stop. Love
me.'

Then she was curled into an exhausted ball,
eyes closed, breathing deep, while she clasped
his hand close to her breast. His arm was
curled around her waist, and he was against
her, chest to back, and slowly, languidly kissing
the nape of her neck. She sighed, throaty and
low, and raised her arm to touch her fingers to
his face.

'How are you?' he asked gently.

'Mm, just fine. How are you?'

She felt his smile against her skin. 'A little
tired.'

That brought a quiet laugh out of her. 'I love
you,' she said, and he buried his face in her hair.

'Then marry me.' She tensed involuntarily,
and knew he had to feel it. He went up on one
elbow. 'Live with me, love me, light up my
mornings with your smile and your kiss. Is it so
hard, sweetheart? Don't you see that it's just a

lifetime of every day, and a moment to moment sharing?'

He made it sound so good and sweet. 'I—don't——' she started, and began to shake all over again.

He dragged her around to face him and said urgently, 'Don't close up on me now.' There was fear in that voice.

She reached out and took hold of his naked shoulder with her free hand, fingers clinging. 'Try your best to understand me,' she whispered. 'I am still afraid. I'm afraid of you, of myself, of our differences and the strange life we would be starting. I—want to say yes, but something always holds me back. What would happen ten years, twenty years later? Would we end up like my parents, tolerating each other but never being happy? Would you be like my father and lose all respect for me while I live through my days, going to parties and luncheons and feeling lonely?'

'Caprice, you are not your mother,' Pierce said patiently. 'Don't you see the qualities you have that come from both your parents? Irene is a very likeable, shallow woman, and you're not shallow at all. And I'm not your father. I'm not reticent. I need and desire your lightness, your jokes and laughter and inconsistencies. I want your soft understanding, and quick retorts. If I wanted someone like myself, I could have found a woman and married her in New York. We would have lived a very serious, very quiet life, and I would have been left wondering what was missing. And in turn, I can offer you a steadiness and emotional security, because I'm not so careless as to let my affection and love for you fade. We're different from each other, nobody disputes that. It isn't bad to be different. It means we'll argue. It means that sometimes we won't understand each other. It means that we'll live a richer, fuller life together than we would apart. You're such a special person. Don't leave my life out of fear.'

Though he couldn't see her expression that well, she buried her face against his chest and said next to his skin, 'You're very persuasive.' Underneath the light tone, the depth of her feeling throbbed.

He relaxed and pressed a kiss to her hair. 'I make it a point to be, with things that are important.'

'OK,' she said, a bare thread of sound, and he quit breathing.

'What did you say? I didn't quite catch that.'

She squirmed closer as if she would burrow right under his skin. 'I said OK! But—just one thing. Please don't tell my mother yet.'

'For God's sake,' he said, and began to laugh. 'Why?'

'Do you know what a fuss she'll make? Let's have peace and quiet while we can, please!'

His fingers dragged through her hair to pull her head back. 'On one condition,' he said sternly. 'You don't decide to change your mind just because of your uncertainties. You come to me, and we'll talk about it.'

She snuggled her face into his warm neck, knowing they would soon have to get up, savouring each fleeting moment. She pressed a kiss to the pulse beating strongly under his jaw. 'Who do I have the feeling that we'll be running up quite a long-distance phone bill?' she murmured.

He hugged her tight. 'Not if we have a quick wedding, we won't. What do you say? Are you set on having a large, fussy white one?'

A large one would be nice, she thought, smiling in the shadows of the quiet room. But it would take so long, and a small one would be more meaningful, more intimate. There were advantages to either idea, and they could really go either way at this stage, as long as her mother didn't find out too soon. Irene would have half the state invited, no doubt about it.

'I don't know,' she said then, doubtfully. 'I guess I'll have to think about it.'

Take 4
Exciting Books
Absolutely
FREE

Love, romance, intrigue... all are captured for you by Mills & Boon's top-selling authors. By becoming a regular reader of Mills & Boon's Romances you can enjoy 6 superb new titles every month plus a whole range of special benefits: your very own personal membership card, a free monthly newsletter packed with recipes, competitions, exclusive book offers and a monthly guide to the stars, plus extra bargain offers and big cash savings.

**AND an Introductory FREE GIFT for YOU.
Turn over the page for details.**

As a special introduction we will send you four
exciting Mills & Boon Romances Free and
without obligation when you complete
and return this coupon.

At the same time we will reserve a subscription to
Mills & Boon Reader Service for you. Every month,
you will receive 6 of the very latest novels by leading
Romantic Fiction authors, delivered direct to your
door. You don't pay extra for delivery — postage and
packing is always completely Free. There is no
obligation or commitment — you can cancel your
subscription at any time.

You have nothing to lose and a whole world of
romance to gain.

Just fill in and post the coupon today to **MILLS & BOON
READER SERVICE, FREEPOST, P.O. BOX 236, CROYDON,
SURREY CR9 9EL**.

Please Note: - READERS IN SOUTH AFRICA write to
Independent Book Services P.T.Y.,
Postbag X3010, Randburg 2125, S. Africa

FREE BOOKS CERTIFICATE

**To: Mills & Boon Reader Service, FREEPOST, P.O. Box 236,
Croydon, Surrey CR9 9EL.**

Please send me, free and without obligation, four Mills & Boon Romances, and reserve a
Reader Service Subscription for me. If I decide to subscribe I shall, from the beginning of the
month following my free parcel of books, receive six new books each month for £7.20, post
and packing free. If I decide not to subscribe, I shall write to you within 10 days. The free books
are mine to keep in any case. I understand that I may cancel my subscription at any time simply
by writing to you. I am over 18 years of age.

Please write in BLOCK CAPITALS.

Signature _____

Name _____

Address _____

_____ Post code _____

SEND NO MONEY — TAKE NO RISKS.

*Mills & Boon reserve the right to exercise discretion in granting
membership. If price changes are necessary you will be notified.
You may be mailed with other offers as a result of this*
6R *application. Offer expires 31st December 1986.*

EPRO